Another Era

A Pictorial History of the School of
Medicine and Biomedical Sciences
State University of New York at Buffalo

——— 1846–1996 ———

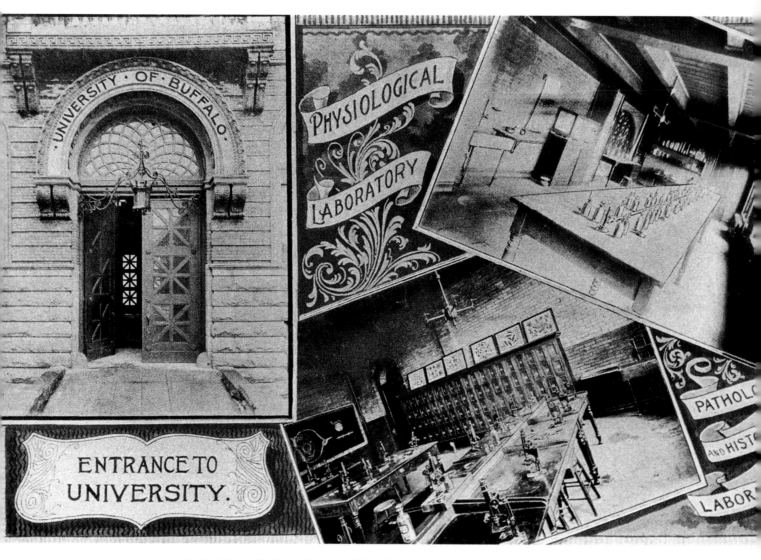

Medical School's former home on High Street, 1898. Courtesy University Archives.

Another Era

A Pictorial History of the School of
Medicine and Biomedical Sciences
State University of New York at Buffalo

1846–1996

Ronald Elmer Batt, M.D., *Department of Gynecology-Obstetrics*

Harold Brody, Ph.D., M.D., *Department of Anatomy and Cell Biology*

Shonnie Finnegan, *University Archivist*

Richard Vaille Lee, M.D., *Department of Medicine*

John Naughton, M.D., *Dean of the School of Medicine and Biomedical Sciences*

Lilli Sentz, *Curator*, Robert L. Brown History of Medicine Collection

Connie Oswald Stofko, *Editorial Associate*

Joyce Váňa, Ph.D., *Department of Social and Preventive Medicine*

THE
DONNING COMPANY
PUBLISHERS

The Donning Company/Publishers
184 Business Park Drive, Suite 106
Virginia Beach, VA 23462

Steve Mull, General Manager
Debra Y. Quesnel, Project Director
Tracey Emmons-Schneider, Director of Research
Mary Jo Kurten, Editor
Joseph Schnellmann, Designer
Dawn V. Kofroth, Production Manager
Tony Lillis, Director of Marketing

Library of Congress Cataloging-in-Publication Data

Another Era: a pictorial history of the School of Medicine and Biomedical Sciences, State University of New York at Buffalo 1846–1996 / Ronald Elmer Batt . . . [et al.].
         p.   cm.
         Includes bibliographical references and index.
         ISBN 0-89865-963-9 (alk. paper)
         1. State University of New York at Buffalo. School of Medicine
and Biomedical Sciences—History. 2. State University of New York at Buffalo,
School of Medicine and Biomedical Sciences —Pictorial works. 3. Medical colleges—
New York (State)—Buffalo—History.
4. Medical colleges—New York (State)—Buffalo—Pictorial works.
I. Batt, Ronald Elmer.
R747.S78P53 1996
610'.71'174797—dc20   95-47775
                                                                            CIP

Printed in the United States of America

Dedication

To the faculty, voluntary and full time, who have served the School and the region.

To the graduates, who use the knowledge and skills they obtained in Buffalo to help people around the world.

Laboratory in the High Street building, 1898. Courtesy University Archives.

Table of Contents

UNIVERSITY AT BUFFALO

SCHOOL OF MEDICINE

150 YEARS

1 8 4 6 - 1 9 9 6

Acknowledgments

We have relied heavily on the resources of the Robert L. Brown History of Medicine Collection at the Health Sciences Library and on the University Archives. The contributions of the twenty-eight departments of the Medical School have also been significant.

We wish to thank those who helped make this book possible: the late Robert L. Brown, former associate dean and Medical School archivist; Christopher Densmore, associate archivist at the University Archives; Earl E. and Margaret S. Jones, archivists at Buffalo General Hospital; Sister Sylvia Flavin, archivist at Sisters Hospital; Mildred Spencer Sanes; the staff of the Buffalo and Erie County Historical Society; the staff of the University's Art and Photographic Services, and the public relations staffs of the affiliated hospitals.

To all our friends,

Greeting ..

Look with charity on our efforts, and if pleasure is found we have our reward.

1899 *Iris*

Introduction

This pictorial history celebrates the sesquicentennial of the School of Medicine and Biomedical Sciences of the State University of New York at Buffalo. In 1992, the Sesquicentennial Committee for the History of the Medical School charged a task force to prepare the volume. This book is our collaborative effort to sketch the story of the School: a story made by many individuals devoted to medicine, to the University, and to the people of Western New York. It is by no means an exhaustive volume, and we are painfully aware that many worthy of mention are not included.

We echo the greeting in the 1899 *Iris*, the student yearbook, and hope you will enjoy the book.

The single greatest factor in the development of the State of New York in the nineteenth century was the Erie Canal. Construction began July 4, 1817, and the canal was completed in 1825. Connecting the Great Lakes to the Hudson River, it provided direct access to New York City. It also stimulated the construction of the railroad system across the state. Buffalo became the main port for the great western migration and prospered as a commercial and industrial center. This print shows barges docked along the canal. Courtesy Buffalo and Erie County Historical Society.

Chapter 1

Founding

Buffalo's first physician, Cyrenius Chapin, came to the region in 1801. The area had just begun to attract immigration and Dr. Chapin quickly established a large practice on both sides of the Niagara River. When Erie County separated out from Niagara County in 1821, the physicians who had settled in the area formed the Medical Society of the County of Erie.

In 1830, the city of Buffalo was a boom town on the Erie Canal, the gateway to the west. Leading citizens proposed that an institution of higher learning be established and, in 1836, the University of Western New York was chartered. However, the newly founded school, primarily organized by Presbyterian clergymen, fell victim to the financial panic of 1837 and closed its doors after only a few months of operation.

Almost ten years later, in 1846, the University of Buffalo was incorporated as a non-sectarian institution. The charter was broad and authorized the University to award degrees in all fields in which degrees were granted by other institutions of higher learning in the country. It also specified that no religious sect was to have a majority on its council.

The founders, primarily physicians and lawyers, intended the University to train students for service to the community. The Medical School, or Medical Department, as it was called, was the first to open. Forty years would pass before other departments were added. Medical classes began February 24, 1847, with an enrollment of sixty-six students.

American medicine at mid-century had changed relatively little since Colonial times. Most medical practitioners had little or no formal education and continued to rely on the therapeutics of heroic medicine: bleeding, blistering, and purging. In protest the public increasingly turned to alternative medicine for treatment.

The proliferation of medical schools and the absence of standards were widely criticized. Austin Flint, a member of the founding faculty of Buffalo, wrote in defense of the establishment of yet another medical school, that medical education could only benefit from free, honorable competition.

This etching shows a view of Buffalo in 1845. Dr. Cornelius Wyckoff, Class of 1848, recollects life in the city as follows: "Our little city lay mostly below Chippewa Street with a few houses straggling out Main, Delaware and Niagara Streets. . . . With houses heated by wood fires, thick frost on the window panes all winter, lighted by candles, using water from wells or brought from a tank-cart, where taking a bath by the kitchen stove was a solemn rite not performed unnecessarily, where a feather bed was a comfort and not an abomination, rooms filled with flies in summer, where cockroaches and the hateful bedbug were, alas, sometimes found, with outdoor privies, heroic in winter, odoriferous at all times—so lived most of the 30,000. Typhoid was common, malaria still occurred, there were several cholera epidemics, some very bad. . . ." Courtesy History of Medicine Collection.

The University was incorporated by an act of the New York State Legislature May 11, 1846. The founders wanted to establish professional schools, but within the broader context of a university as diversified as any in the land. Departments of law, theology, and liberal arts were contemplated. However, the Medical School remained the only department for forty years. Courtesy New York State Archives.

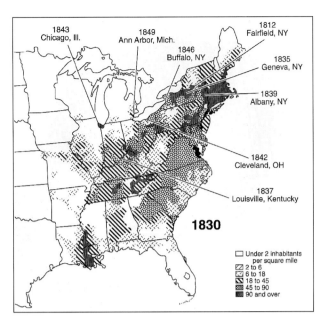

Successive waves of migration and changes in population density led to the founding of medical schools across New York State. In 1812, the first medical school opened in Upstate New York at Fairfield Medical School, Herkimer County, not far from Utica. Later, medical schools were established in Albany and Geneva. When the Medical Department, University of Buffalo, was founded in 1846, it drew not only students from Geneva, but five of its most notable faculty. Eventually, it became clear that small towns such as Geneva could not sustain a medical school. The schools that survived were located in large population centers where the possibilities for growth, clinical training, and financial support were much greater. Courtesy Richard V. Lee, M.D.

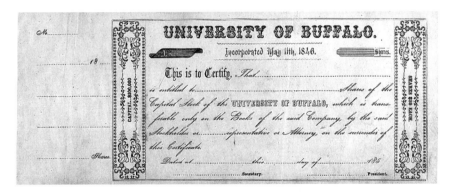

Almost a quarter of the $100,000 in capital authorized for the University was raised by selling stock, a common practice. Each share cost $20 and 1,009 shares were sold. The biggest stockholders were two members of the founding faculty—Dr. Austin Flint and Dr. Frank H. Hamilton. Each bought 403 shares. Millard Fillmore, who later became president of the United States, was one of several individuals who bought a single share. Like other proprietary schools of the time, the Medical School operated on tuition fees alone. There was no endowment, and funding for necessary buildings and property was to be raised by public subscription. No dividends were paid and all of the stock was signed back to the University by 1909. The only meeting ever held by the stockholders was to elect the governing body, the University Council. Courtesy University Archives

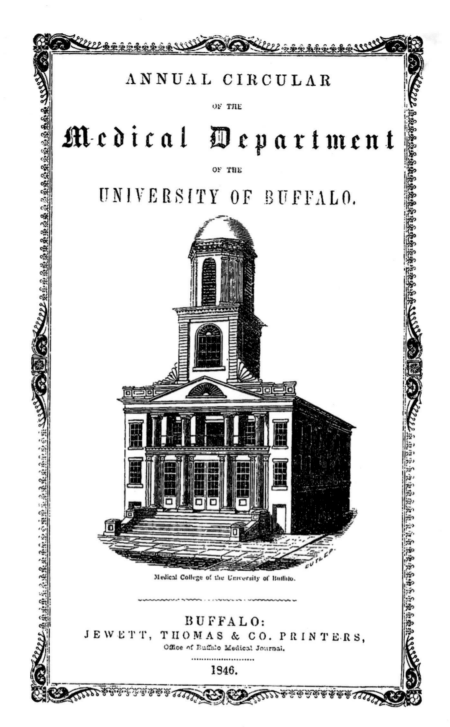

ANNUAL CIRCULAR

OF THE

Medical Department

OF THE

UNIVERSITY OF BUFFALO.

Medical College of the University of Buffalo.

BUFFALO:
JEWETT, THOMAS & CO. PRINTERS,
Office of Buffalo Medical Journal.

1846.

As the first home of the Medical School, the University rented a building at the corner of Washington and Seneca Streets for $300 a year. Originally the First Baptist Church, the wooden structure was built in 1829 and later functioned as a customs office, a post office, and a court. The building was well suited as a temporary site for the Medical School and included a lecture room, a museum, a library, and a laboratory. The amphitheater accommodated up to two hundred students and also served as the dispensary. The dispensary, which was open for surgery, medical consultations, and dispensing of medicines, was free to indigent patients and patients willing to appear before a medical school class. Courtesy University Archives.

The first seal of the University incorporated the elements of the greater university as envisioned by the founding faculty. The seal pictured Hippocrates, the father of medicine, surrounded by the symbols of law, theology, and liberal arts as well as the caduceus. Courtesy History of Medicine Collection.

Millard Fillmore became the first chancellor of the University, a post he held during his presidency of the United States and until his death in 1874. The primary obligations of the chancellor were to preside at commencement and at meetings of the council. After his national political career ended, President Fillmore devoted his time to Buffalo's cultural, educational, and philanthropic institutions. Today, the evening division of the University is named in his honor. Courtesy University Archives.

Founding Faculty

According to Harvey Cushing, renowned neurosurgeon, the founding faculty of the Medical Department, University of Buffalo, was as notable a faculty of energetic men as one could hope to find anywhere. They came to Buffalo with highly diverse training and backgrounds. Five of them were recruited from Geneva Medical College where they continued to teach during the fall semester. Dr. Cornelius Wyckoff, Class of 1848, gave the following vivid description of his professors: "I wish I could present to you a graphic picture of these first seven professors as they appear to me in memory—the dignified and serious Hadley . . . ; the courtly Christian gentleman, Professor Coventry, whose innate modesty put him to the blush upon demonstrating his obstetrical lectures upon the manikin; the agile and oftentimes brilliant Hamilton, entering the amphitheater almost on a run, lecturing as he came, and seeming only desirous of improving every moment to give us the benefit of his vast store of learning; the more dignified Flint, who at the beginning of his career as a lecturer was somewhat inclined to verboseness, but who afterward attained an eminence in this branch of his profession as may make us justly proud of having given him to the world; the daring White, who raised such a storm of abuse, which he manfully met, when he introduced 'demonstrative midwifery;' the companionable, convivial Webster, who was masterly at dissection, lecturing as rapidly as the scalpel cut into the tissues of the subject, never for a moment at a loss for words to explain the hidden course of nature. Oftentimes Dr. LaFord would have to perform the duties of a lecturer as well as those of a demonstrator of anatomy, but it was at no loss to the students. Professor Lee was perhaps less known to us, as he always retained his home in New York but his uniform kindness made him popular, although his subject was dry and prosy." Photos of the founding faculty courtesy History of Medicine Collection

Professor of Obstetrics and Diseases of Women and Children

Credited by Austin Flint as the individual most responsible for the founding of the Medical School, James Platt White served as the first professor of obstetrics and diseases of women and children, and remained a member of the faculty until his death. Dr. White was born in Austerlitz, Columbia County, New York, and began initially to study law at Middlebury Academy. After hearing a course of lectures on physiology, he turned his interest to medicine. Dr. White attended lectures at Fairfield Medical School and at Jefferson Medical College in Philadelphia, where he was graduated in 1834. He moved to Buffalo and for the next ten years practiced as a surgeon and obstetrician/gynecologist. He was instrumental in founding the early hospitals as well as the Young Men's Association, the Academy of Fine Arts, and the Buffalo Historical Society.

James Platt White, M.D.
(1811–1881)

Professor of Principles and Practice of Medicine and Clinical Medicine

The most distinguished member of the founding faculty, Austin Flint became the first registrar and treasurer of the Medical School. Dr. Flint was born in Petersham, Massachusetts, in 1812, the fourth generation of physicians. He received his undergraduate education at Amherst and Harvard and graduated from Harvard Medical School in 1833. He moved to Buffalo in 1836 and was instrumental in attracting distinguished members of the faculty at Geneva Medical College to Buffalo. He was also the founder, owner, and editor of the *Buffalo Medical Journal*. He moved permanently from Buffalo in 1859 and ended his illustrious career as professor of principles and practice of medicine and clinical medicine at Bellevue Hospital Medical College in New York City.

Austin Flint, M.D.
(1812–1886)

Professor of Physiology and Medical Jurisprudence

Born near Utica, New York, Charles Brodhead Coventry apprenticed in his father's office and, after attending lectures at Fairfield Medical School, he received his medical degree in 1825. When Geneva Medical College was founded in 1834, Dr. Coventry was persuaded to accept the chair of materia medica and obstetrics. He continued to teach at Geneva until, twelve years later, he accepted the chair of physiology and medical jurisprudence at Buffalo. At the same time, he also kept an extensive family practice in Utica, which was interrupted each year when he left for Geneva and Buffalo. He resigned his post in 1851 and became the first faculty member to be nominated emeritus professor.

Charles Brodhead
Coventry, M.D.
(1801–1875)

Frank Hastings Hamilton,
M.D. (1813–1886)

Professor of Principles and Practice of Surgery and Clinical Surgery

Frank Hastings Hamilton served as the first dean of the Medical School. Born in Wilmington, Vermont, in 1813, he graduated from Union College and became a medical apprentice to John G. Morgan, surgeon at the Auburn State Prison. He attended lectures at Fairfield Medical School and received his medical degree from the University of Pennsylvania in 1835. He was appointed professor of surgery at Fairfield Medical School and at Geneva Medical College. In 1844 he established residence in Buffalo and, together with James Platt White and Austin Flint, was instrumental in founding the Medical School. Dr. Hamilton remained in Buffalo as professor of surgery for fourteen years until he accepted the post of professor of surgery at the Long Island College Hospital in Brooklyn and later at Bellevue Hospital Medical College. In 1861 he was appointed a medical director in the Army of the Potomac and, two years later, medical inspector of the United States Army. He resigned his professorship at Bellevue in 1875, but remained a visiting surgeon there and at other city dispensaries until his death in 1886.

George Hadley, M.D.
(1813–1877)

Professor of Chemistry and Pharmacy

George Hadley graduated from Hamilton College in 1834 and received his medical degree from Fairfield Medical School in 1839. His chief interests were chemistry and metallurgy. In 1846, he was appointed professor of chemistry and pharmacy at the University of Buffalo, a position he held until his death thirty-one years later.

James Webster, M D
(1803–1854)

Professor of General and Special Anatomy

James Webster was born in England and moved with his family to Philadelphia as a small boy. He received his M.D. from the University of Pennsylvania in 1824. Webster acquired a reputation as an eloquent teacher of anatomy and a skillful surgeon and taught in Philadelphia and New York City before accepting the position as chair of anatomy and physiology at Geneva Medical College. When the University of Buffalo was founded he was appointed professor of general and special anatomy. He resigned his post in 1851 and died three years later from heart disease.

Demonstrator of Anatomy and Librarian

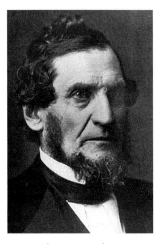

Corydon LaFord, M.D.
(1813–1894)

Corydon LaFord, born near Lexington, Greene County, New York, taught elementary school for eight years while apprenticing with two physicians. He studied medicine at Geneva Medical College and supported himself by serving as librarian and curator of the museum at the same time. He attracted the attention of James Webster, and when Dr. Webster became professor of general and special anatomy in Buffalo, Dr. LaFord was appointed demonstrator of anatomy and librarian. A highly effective teacher, Dr. LaFord was commended in a resolution passed by the students as "unsurpassed." Dr. LaFord remained in Buffalo until 1851. Three years later he was appointed professor of anatomy at the University of Michigan, a position he held for forty years. During vacations he lectured at schools throughout the Northeast. Few professors of medicine in the country instructed as many students as did Dr. LaFord.

Professor of Pathology and Materia Medica

Charles Alfred Lee, M.D.
(1801–1872)

Born in Salisbury, Connecticut, Charles Alfred Lee attended Williams College and, after apprenticing in the office of his brother-in-law, graduated from Berkshire Medical College in 1825. He practiced medicine in New York City until he accepted his first academic appointment in 1844 at Geneva Medical College. In 1846, Dr. Lee was appointed professor of pathology and materia medica at Buffalo. He held the dual appointment until 1856, when he resigned from pathology, but continued teaching materia medica until he was named emeritus professor in 1871.

Medical College of the University of Buffalo.

The regular courses of lectures in this institution, will commence on Friday of this week, and will continue to the end of the term—16 weeks. For the present, we are authorized to say, the lectures will be delivered in the following order :

Dr. WEBSTER, on Anatomy, at 9, A. M., and 2, P. M., each day.

Dr. HADLEY, on Chemistry, at 10, A. M., each day, except Wednesday and Saturday.

Dr. HAMILTON, on Surgery, at 11, A. M., each day.

Dr. FLINT, on Practice of Medicine, at 3, P. M., each day, and also at 10, A. M., on Wednesday and Saturday.   No lectures will be delivered Saturday afternoon.

Public introductory lectures will be given on Wednesday, tomorrow, by Dr. FLINT, at 2, P.M., and Dr. HAMILTON at 3, P. M., and on Thursday by Dr. HADLEY, at 2, P. M., and Dr. WEBSTER at 3, P. M.   Ladies and gentlemen are invited to attend.

DISPENSARY.—At 12 o'clock of each day, during the term, surgical counsel will be given and operations made, free of charge, before the class, upon such as are unable to pay.—At 4 o'clock of each day medical counsel will be given, and medicines administered free of charge to the poor.

The first lecture was presented in the spring of 1847. Students attended two terms of lectures lasting sixteen weeks each in the following subjects: surgery, principles and practice of medicine, chemistry and pharmacy, anatomy, obstetrics and diseases of women and children, physiology, medical jurisprudence, and pathology and materia medica. Courtesy University Archives.

I **Certify**, That *Henry A. Tingley* has pursued the study of Medicine and Surgery under my direction, from the *first* ____ day of *November* in the year *1846* to the *fifth* day of *May* in the year *1847*, and that he is of good moral character.

Dated at *Albany* this *fifth* day of *May 1847*

J. Schermerhorn MD

Each medical student had to prove that he had served a three-year apprenticeship with a licensed physician. Most received a simple handwritten letter from the preceptor. A formal certificate such as the one pictured was rare. In 1846, many physicians had been trained through apprenticeship without the benefit of a university education. Some apprentices received a thorough training while others found themselves greasing the doctor's carriage, feeding the horse, or running errands for the doctor's wife. Courtesy University Archives.

University of Buffalo.

MEDICAL DEPARTMENT.

Principles and Practice of Medicine.

By Austin Flint, M. D.

Session 1848-9.

For *F. F. Hoyer.*

Students paid fees to the professors—sixty-five dollars for all courses plus a three-dollar matriculation fee—and received a ticket admitting them to the lectures. Fees were the only source of income for the University aside from fund-raising drives for buildings. Professors kept the profits and made up deficits. Millard Fillmore commented that if the professors felt they were not making enough money they should recruit more students, and that any professor who could not support himself by teaching must be incompetent. Courtesy History of Medicine Collection.

THE

BUFFALO

MEDICAL JOURNAL.

EDITED BY
AUSTIN FLINT, M. D.

VOLUME FIRST.

BUFFALO,
JEWETT, THOMAS & CO. PRINTERS,
Office of Commercial Advertiser.
1846.

For seventy-four years, the *Buffalo Medical Journal* recorded the principal medical events in Erie County. Founded in 1845 by Dr. Austin Flint, the *Journal* included original scientific articles, case histories, book summaries and reviews, proceedings of local organizations, and obituaries. During World War I, the number of contributions to the *Journal* declined and in 1919 it ceased publication. Courtesy History of Medicine Collection.

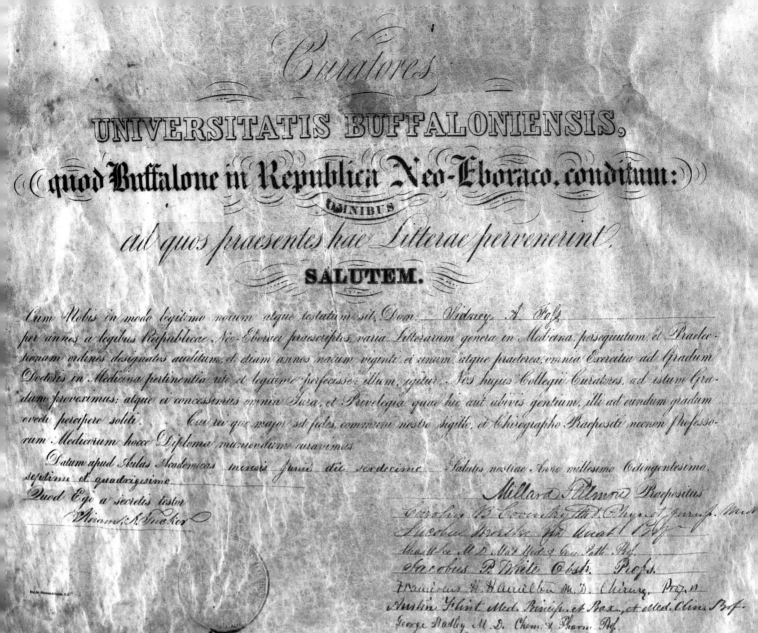

Illustrated here is one of the diplomas issued by the Medical School at its first commencement in June 1847. Seventeen students were awarded medical degrees. A graduate had to be at least twenty-two years old, be of good moral character, write a dissertation on a medical subject, have attended two terms of lectures of sixteen weeks each, and have apprenticed with a regular physician for three years. These requirements approximated those at other medical schools, including Harvard, Yale, the University of New York, and the University of Pennsylvania. Courtesy University Archives.

Just three years after its founding, the Medical School moved from its rented quarters into its own building. The edifice, located on the corner of Main and Virginia Streets, was completed in 1849 at a cost of $15,000. It was the first building in Buffalo constructed for the purpose of collegiate instruction. Built in Romanesque style, the red sandstone building had small spires at each corner and was described as one of the best designed medical school buildings in the country. Courtesy University Archives.

26

Chapter 2

Early Years

When the Medical School opened, clinical instruction took place at a public dispensary in the School and at the Erie County Almshouse. The first Annual Circular, or school catalog, had optimistically announced that teaching would be conducted at the Buffalo City Hospital. Unfortunately, organizers were unable to obtain financial support from New York State and the hospital was not built. One public official in Albany declared it was time the western part of the state began to look out for its own interests. There was also considerable local opposition to the plan.

In order to fill the need, the Sisters of Charity opened a hospital in Buffalo in 1848. The rapid growth of the city made a second hospital necessary and in 1858, Buffalo General Hospital was dedicated.

In his *History of Medical Education in the United States before the Civil War*, William F. Norwood contended that upstate and western schools, although weak in clinical instruction, were redeemed by extraordinary faculties. This was especially true in Buffalo. Highlighted in the following pages are the contributions of members of the faculty and graduates who achieved national and international fame during the School's formative years.

The Erie County Almshouse, a home for the poor, was established in 1829 in a small stone building on Porter Avenue. It could accommodate up to two hundred people. In the mid-nineteenth century, the almshouse was moved to "Buffalo Plains" at the edge of the city. In 1874, a hospital for the insane was added. That building, at right, is now Hayes Hall on the University's South Campus at Main and Bailey. Courtesy History of Medicine Collection.

The prescription laboratory, shown here, was located on the top floor of the new Medical School. The center of the building held two large rooms: the anatomical amphitheater and the College Hall, or general lecture room. Each could seat almost four hundred people. The building also contained a spacious and well designed dissecting room, a library, and a museum. Courtesy University Archives.

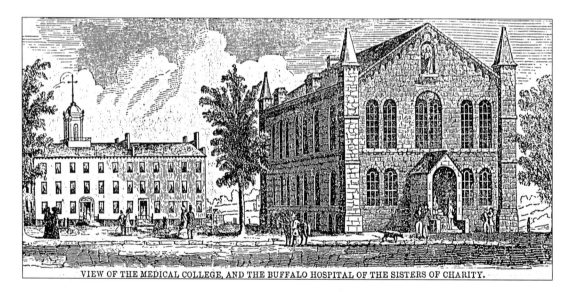

VIEW OF THE MEDICAL COLLEGE, AND THE BUFFALO HOSPITAL OF THE SISTERS OF CHARITY.

In August 1848, the Sisters of Charity opened a hospital, shown at left, the first in Buffalo to be organized on a permanent basis and the first teaching hospital. Located near the Medical School, which is seen at right, the three and-one-half-story building was bought by Bishop John Timon from the Buffalo Orphan Asylum. The medical board included Drs. Hamilton, Flint, and White, and treatment was open to individuals of all religious denominations. By 1872, the hospital had outgrown its premises and a new site was purchased on Main and Delavan. The hospital was one of the first under the management of the Sisters of Charity to institute the practice of educating resident physicians. Courtesy University Archives.

In 1860, Austin Flint sold his two-story farmhouse located at the junction of Main Street and Scajaquada Creek to the Sisters of Charity, who built an institution for the mentally ill on the grounds. Today the Sisters of Charity Hospital occupies this site. Courtesy History of Medicine Collection.

Several attempts to found a nondenominational hospital had failed. In 1855 a group of interested citizens met again and this time incorporation papers were filed. Located between High and Goodrich Streets, the Buffalo General Hospital was finally dedicated in June 1858. For many years the hospital was plagued by lack of capital, but by 1880 sufficient funds had been secured and a much needed wing was added. Courtesy Buffalo General Hospital Archives.

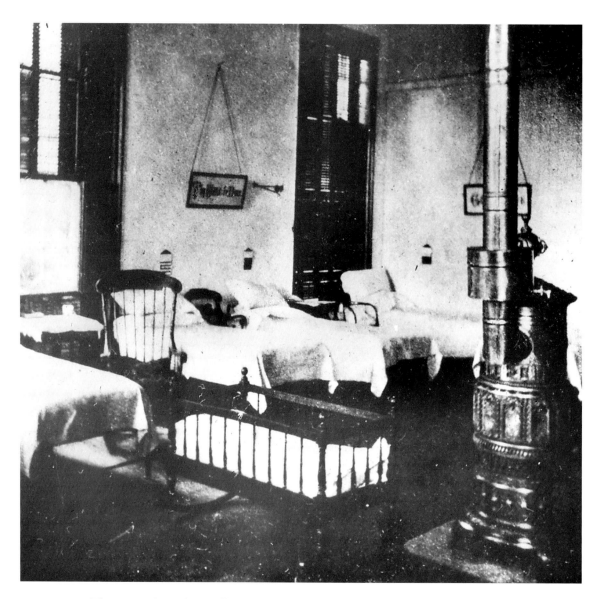

This women's ward at Buffalo General Hospital in 1886 was heated by a coal stove. The water for the building had to be drawn in a water cart from the corner of Main and Virginia Streets, emptied into a large cistern, and pumped through the building. Courtesy Buffalo General Hospital Archives.

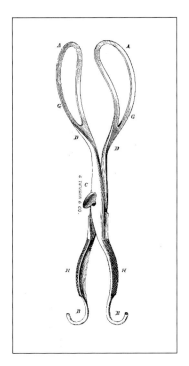

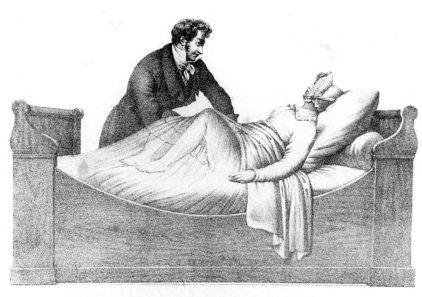

Touching in the horizontal posture.

Left: Dr. James Platt White was a pioneer in American obstetrics and gynecology. He introduced the clinical teaching of obstetrics in the United States, advocated the use of anesthesia in childbirth, and was responsible for the development of many new surgical techniques and instruments, including an obstetrical forceps shown here. Courtesy History of Medicine Collection.

Right: On January 18, 1850, Dr. White conducted before a class of twenty students the first clinical demonstration of a live birth in the United States. Demonstrative midwifery had been part of the medical curriculum in Europe for some time, and Dr. White felt that students should witness at least one delivery before entering practice. In the United States, doctors modestly performed vaginal exams beneath the bedclothes, shown here, and did not see babies enter the world. The demonstration caused an outcry in the city and the popular press nationwide took sides for and against Dr. White. Dr. Horatio Loomis was especially pleased with an editorial in the *Buffalo Courier* critical of Dr. White. He purchased eight hundred copies and circulated them widely. Dr. White sued him for libel. Although Dr. Loomis was acquitted, the practice of demonstrative midwifery was vindicated and, in spite of opposition by the American Medical Association, slowly entered the curriculum of medical schools across the country. Drawing from *Midwifery Illustrated* by J. P. Maygrier. New York: J. K. Moore, 1833.

In the fall of 1843, an outbreak of fever occurred in North Boston, a small village eight miles south of Buffalo. Of the forty-three inhabitants, twenty-eight became ill and ten died. Austin Flint led an investigation and traced the source of the outbreak to a contaminated well at Fuller's Tavern, pictured here. Concluding that the disease was typhoid fever, which had been brought to North Boston by a traveler, Dr. Flint prophesied that in due time the functions of a physician would embrace not only treatment, but also prevention of disease. Courtesy History of Medicine Collection.

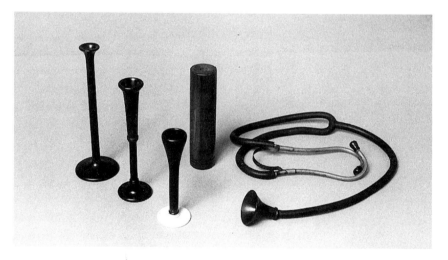

Austin Flint was a superb clinician. He was considered the "American Laënnec" for his advocacy of the binaural stethoscope, an improvement over the earlier monaural models at left. He was also known as the "Nestor of American Medicine" for his extensive experience and wisdom gained from a long career as practitioner and teacher. His many clinical contributions included the description of the cardiac murmur that bears his name. He authored more than two hundred articles and sixteen books. His treatise entitled *Principles and Practice of Medicine*, first published in 1866, was described in a contemporary review as the book most likely to be found in the office of a physician, whether in city, town, or village. Courtesy History of Medicine Collection.

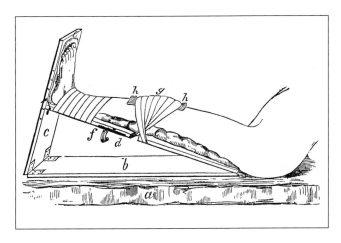

Published in 1860, Frank Hastings Hamilton's famous book on fractures went through eight editions and was translated into French and German. The illustration shows the dressing of a fractured patella. In 1854, Dr. Hamilton performed the first successful skin grafting operation by transporting a piece of skin seven by four inches from the left leg of a patient to an ulcer on the patient's right leg. Courtesy History of Medicine Collection.

Left: John C. Dalton (1825–1889), pupil of French physiologist Claude Bernard and one of the most influential American physiologists of the nineteenth century, was present at the first surgical demonstration of ether in Boston, Massachusetts, in 1846. He was intrigued by the possible use of anesthesia in vivisection and, when he became professor of physiology at Buffalo in 1851, began illustrating his lectures through vivisection. The practice was widely criticized and, in his own defense, Dr. Dalton published the famous treatise *Experimental Method in Medical Science.* Courtesy History of Medicine Collection.

Right: Thomas F. Rochester (1823–1887) made significant contributions to our understanding of appendicitis. Born in Rochester, New York, he was the grandson of Colonel Nathaniel Rochester, for whom the city of Rochester is named. Dr. Rochester practiced medicine in New York City before moving to Buffalo in 1853 to become professor of principles and practice of medicine and clinical medicine, the chair vacated by Austin Flint. He was a member of the Medical School faculty until 1887 and served as its dean three times. Courtesy History of Medicine Collection.

The faculty of the Medical School in 1861 consisted of, from left, seated, James Platt White, Edward Mott Moore, Sandford Eastman, and Charles Alfred Lee. From left, standing, George Hadley, Thomas F. Rochester, and William H. Mason. Courtesy University Archives.

The Buffalo General Hospital was officially designated a United States Army General Hospital on December 1, 1863. Earlier in the year, the hospital received nearly one hundred soldiers from New England regiments involved in the Civil War, many of whom were totally exhausted and more than half of whom died. Courtesy Buffalo General Hospital Archives.

Toward the end of the Civil War, the four wards of Buffalo General Hospital were so overcrowded it was necessary to erect tents on the hospital grounds to accommodate the wounded. Courtesy Buffalo General Hospital Archives.

One soldier, Devillo W. Harrington (1844–1905), lay wounded on the battlefield for three days before being evacuated. When he arrived at Buffalo General Hospital, his case was considered hopeless. The interns tried a new dressing of permanganate of potash, one of the first antiseptic surgical dressings used, and the patient recovered. Dr. Harrington graduated from the Medical School in 1871 and later became the first professor of genitourinary and venereal diseases at the University. To commemorate the twenty-fifth anniversary of his graduation, Dr. Harrington established an endowment. For a full century, the Harrington Lectureship has brought outstanding medical scientists to Buffalo. Here, Dr. Harrington is shown at left with Warden William Bagley in the physicians' room at Buffalo General Hospital. Courtesy Buffalo General Hospital Archives.

Julius F. Miner (1823–1886) moved to Buffalo in 1855 and quickly established himself as a bold and original surgeon. He was the first to perform successfully the operation of thyroidectomy and also demonstrated the principle of enucleation in the removal of ovarian tumors, a method that was adopted universally. Dr. Miner joined the faculty of the Medical School in 1867 and served as dean from 1870 to 1875. In 1861 he re-established the *Buffalo Medical Journal,* founded by Austin Flint, and continued to edit the *Journal* for many years. Courtesy History of Medicine Collection.

William Warren Potter (1838–1911) graduated from the University of Buffalo in 1859 and served as lieutenant-colonel during the Civil War. After the war, Dr. Potter practiced medicine in Buffalo. He was instrumental in establishing the New York State Medical Examining Board and served as its president for fourteen years. Dr. Potter was a talented writer. He edited the *Buffalo Medical Journal* from 1888 until his death in 1911 and wrote a series of articles on Buffalo's medical history, which were published in the *Journal* in time for the celebration of the fiftieth anniversary of the Medical School in 1896. Here he is pictured in his uniform some time after the war. Courtesy History of Medicine Collection.

An 1851 Medical School graduate, Albert J. Myer (1827–1880) achieved national distinction. Dr. Myer worked as a telegraph operator during his student years, a skill that led to his lifelong interest in communications. In 1854, he entered the United States Army as an assistant surgeon and devised a signaling system using flags by day and torches by night. When the Signal Corps of the Army was founded, he was appointed signal officer with the rank of major. After the Civil War, Dr. Myer was assigned to make meteorological observations available to the public and he laid the foundations for the National Weather Service as we know it today. He died in Buffalo in 1880 of Bright's disease and is buried in Forest Lawn Cemetery. This daguerreotype, believed to have been made in 1854, is courtesy U.S. Army Signal Corps Museum.

Margaretta Fox Kane

Left: In 1848 it was reported that spirits were communicating with two girls, Margaret Fox, then age thirteen, shown here, and her sister Katherine, eleven, who lived near Rochester. Strange rapping sounds were heard in the presence of the girls. Margaret began to give public demonstrations across the state, charging an entrance fee of one dollar. A team of three physicians from the Medical School consisting of Drs. Flint, Lee, and Coventry examined the two girls and concluded that the sound originated in Margaret's knee joints. Although the findings were widely publicized, the sisters denied the hoax and continued to win converts to spiritualism. Katherine denounced spiritualism in the 1870s, but Margaret did not confess the fraud until 1888, when she revealed that they made the noise with their toes. Picture from *Modern Spiritualism* by A. Leah Underhill. New York: Thomas R. Knox, 1885.

Right: John Davidson Hill (1822–1892) attended the University of Buffalo from January 31, 1848, to April 18, 1849. As a medical student and also later during the cholera epidemic of 1852, he kept a diary and recorded in detail his impressions of the founding faculty, student life, and the epidemic. Dr. Hill, who had graduated at the top of his class, attracted notoriety in 1855 when he, along with a colleague, Dr. Gray, was expelled from the Erie County Medical Society for rendering services for less than specified in the association's fee schedule. Both physicians appealed to the New York State Supreme Court and were reinstated. Thirty years later Dr. Hill was elected president of the society. Courtesy History of Medicine Collection.

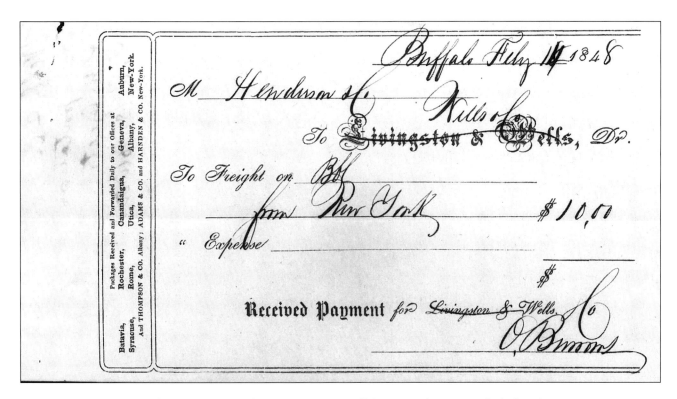

Buffalo Feby 14 1848

M Henderson &

To Livingston & Wells, Dr.

To Freight on Bbl

from New York $10,00

" Expense

$

Received Payment for Livingston & Wells.

The first known case of grave robbing in Buffalo occurred nine months before the University was founded. Three men, including a physician, were arrested for attempting to ship bodies to Willoughby Medical College in Ohio for profit. Two barrels containing four bodies pickled in alcohol brine were recovered. In the early years of the School, cadavers for dissection were difficult to obtain and it was necessary for the Medical School to use great discretion in order to procure anatomical subjects. The bill of lading shown above from Wells & Co. was carefully marked on the back "transportation of subjects" by Dr. Flint. Courtesy University Archives.

MEDICAL DEPARTMENT
UNIVERSITY OF BUFFALO

39ᵀᴴ ANNUAL COMMENCEMENT
COMPLIMENTS OF THE
GRADUATING CLASS
CONCERT HALL,
TUESDAY. FEBᵞ 24ᵀᴴ 7.30 P.M. 1885.

PRESIDENT.	**VICE PRESIDENT.**
F. S. COMFORT.	G. W. McCLELAN.
SECRETARY.	**TREASURER.**
Sarah E. Simonet.	M. B. Huff.
ORATOR.	**MARSHAL.**
Charles Kennedy.	W. E. Robbins.
EX. COMMITTEE.	**COM. ON MUSIC.**
C. S. Logan.	L. B. Andrews.
J. F. Sherman.	A. E. Campbell
F. F. Dow.	G. E. Alexander.

Chapter 3

Growing

The transformation of American medicine in the second half of the nineteenth century had profound repercussions for the medical community in Western New York. The introduction of anesthesia and antisepsis, the establishment of the germ theory of disease, and the development of the x-ray revolutionized medical practice.

In Buffalo, new hospitals were established and the existing ones, Sisters Hospital and Buffalo General Hospital, expanded greatly. The Medical School curriculum was no longer adequate to train physicians in the basic sciences and new clinical advances. In 1883 Niagara University founded a competing medical department in the city of Buffalo, dividing the loyalties of the community until the two schools merged in 1898.

The recruitment of the surgeon Roswell Park in 1883, the decision to build a modern medical school building, and the establishment of departments of pharmacy, law, and dentistry at the University provided new optimism.

At the turn of the century the city of Buffalo had more than 300,000 inhabitants, ten times as many as when the Medical School was founded. It was the terminus of lake and canal navigation and an important railroad center. The Pan American Exposition, which opened in Buffalo on May 1, 1901, was one of the most imaginative of the great fairs popular at that time. Promoting New World cultural and economic unity, the fair attempted to present the enterprise, education, art, and general business progress of the Western Hemisphere. Electricity was the theme and the exposition boasted the largest display of electrical machinery and appliances the world had ever seen. A medical pavilion complete with x-ray equipment, operating table, sterilizing appliances, and instruments was constructed and functioned as the emergency hospital.

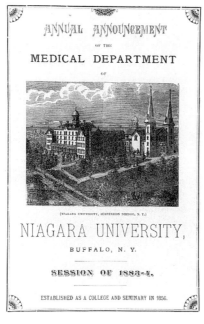

In 1883, an event of great significance for medical education in Buffalo took place. The Seminary of Our Lady of Angels, located on the banks of the Niagara River near Lewiston since 1863, changed its name to Niagara University, pictured at left. It enlarged its charter and established a rival medical school in the city of Buffalo, pictured above. Partly in response to the general criticism of American medical education, the new school offered a three-year curriculum, one year more than at the University of Buffalo, and instituted more stringent entrance requirements. A distinguished teaching faculty was appointed and Sisters Hospital served as the teaching hospital.

Four years earlier a homeopathic school, the Buffalo College of Rational Medicine, had opened for classes. It changed name and address several times and was closed in 1883 by a court order for not being legally incorporated. Courtesy History of Medicine Collection.

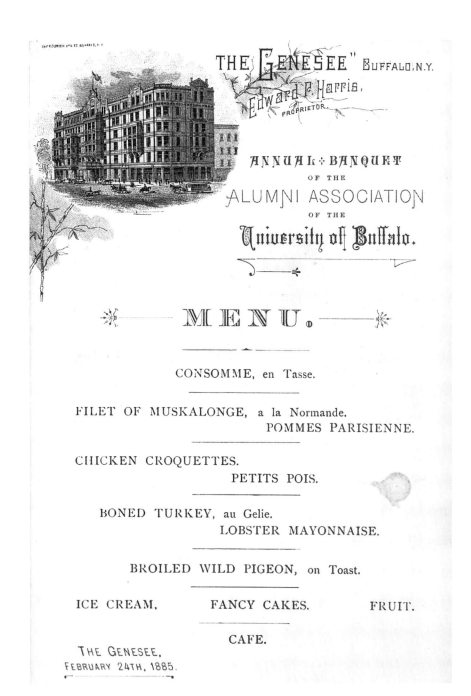

THE "GENESEE" BUFFALO, N.Y.
Edward P. Harris, PROPRIETOR.

ANNUAL ✦ BANQUET
OF THE
ALUMNI ASSOCIATION
OF THE
University of Buffalo.

MENU.

CONSOMME, en Tasse.

FILET OF MUSKALONGE, a la Normande.
POMMES PARISIENNE.

CHICKEN CROQUETTES.
PETITS POIS.

BONED TURKEY, au Gelie.
LOBSTER MAYONNAISE.

BROILED WILD PIGEON, on Toast.

ICE CREAM,   FANCY CAKES.   FRUIT.

CAFE.

THE GENESEE,
FEBRUARY 24TH, 1885.

The commencement program for the Class of 1885, which had forty-seven members, is shown on page 40. The alumni sponsored a sumptuous banquet the same day.

The qualifications for graduation had changed little during the previous forty years. In 1891, however, a state law was adopted that stipulated three years of medical school as a minimum for graduation. In addition, the University of Buffalo required that the candidate be at least twenty-one years old, of good moral character, have written a thesis on a medical subject, and completed a three-year preceptorship under a regular physician. To enter medical school, students had to pass, at a minimum, an examination according to the standards of the Regents of the University of the State of New York in arithmetic, grammar, geography, spelling, American history, English composition and natural philosophy. Courtesy University Archives.

UNIVERSITY OF BUFFALO----Medical Department.
SCHEDULE OF LECTURES.——Session 1897-8.
FRESHMAN CLASS.

HRS.	MONDAY.	TUESDAY.	WEDNESDAY	THURSDAY.	FRIDAY.	SATURDAY.
9 A.M.		Physiology.	Anatomy.	Physiology.		Physiology.
10 A.M.	Anatomy	Hygiene. Nov. 8th.	Chemistry		Anatomy.	
11 A.M.	Anatomy Quiz.		Recitation.			
2 P.M.		Histological			Chemistry	
3 P.M.	Histological	Laboratory	Biology.	Histology Recitation.	Recitation.	
4 P.M.	Laboratory			Anatomy Quiz.		
5 P.M.						
8 P. M.	Dissection.					

When the Medical School was founded, two sixteen-week terms of classes were stipulated, the second term merely a repeat of the first. By 1897, students were required to attend three full years of medical school. Illustrated above is the demanding and varied schedule of lectures for freshman students. Courtesy University Archives.

UNIVERSITY OF BUFFALO.

MEDICAL DEPARTMENT.

Senior Class, April, 1899.

THERAPEUTICS.

1. Explain the action of counter-irritants and illustrate fully their uses.

2. Digitalis. Define the drug. Name two official preparations with their doses.
      State its action upon the circulation.
      State its action upon elimination.
      State rational contra-indications to its use.

3. Name the active ingredients of (a) Dover's Powder, (b) Tully's Powder, (c) Compound Licorice Powder, (d) Compound Jalap Powder.

4. State special therapeutic value and dose of each.

5. Explain the value of high altitudes in the treatment of Phthisis. State contra-indications.

6. Give symptoms and treatment of poisoning by Strychnine Sulphate.

7. Discuss the use of Ergot in the treatment of hemorrhages.

8. Give the rational treatment of convulsions occurring during the period of first dentition.

9. State the therapeutic uses of Nitroglycerin. Give name, strength and dose of its official preparation.

10. Write a prescription for ten anodyne suppositories to be used in the treatment of Dysentery in an adult. What treatment should precede their use?

This 1899 therapeutics exam covers some preparations, such as digitalis for heart disease, ergot for controlling postpartum hemorrhage, and nitroglycerin for angina, that are still used today. But what modern doctor could answer question three? According to Ann M. Triggle and Dr. Leo Fedor of the School of Pharmacy, the Dover's Powder was used as a diaphoretic (to produce perspiration) and as a sedative. The active ingredients were ipecac powder and powdered opium, which could indeed make a patient sleep unless vomiting kept him awake. Tully's Powder, made with morphine to relieve pain, camphor to produce a feeling of warmth, and licorice flavoring, was probably used for teething. Compound Licorice Powder was used as a cathartic (laxative) and contained senna, glycyrrhiza, sulphur, and oil of fennel. Compound Jalap Powder was also used as a cathartic and contained powdered jalap root and potassium bitartrate. In question six, it was important to recognize an overdose of strychnine sulphate because it was used as a tonic—the bitter taste was supposed to stimulate appetite—and was also used to treat barbiturate poisoning. In 1899, a new drug was added to the physician's arsenal—aspirin. Courtesy University Archives.

When Roswell Park (1852–1914) was recruited from Rush Medical College in Chicago in 1883 to the position of professor of surgery, his appointment was not uniformly welcomed by Buffalo's medical community. There was widespread chagrin that a locally trained and practicing surgeon had not been appointed. However, Dr. Park's professional talents and personal attributes soon made him one of the most influential members of the medical community.

Dr. Park was born in Pomfret, Connecticut, in 1852 and received his medical degree from Northwestern University in 1876. He interned at Cook County Hospital and also studied in Germany, France, and Austria before accepting the position in Buffalo. Throughout his career he received many flattering offers to move to prestigious institutions elsewhere, but decided that his loyalties were in Buffalo. Although his great ambition to know the cause of cancer was not realized, it led to the establishment in 1898 of the New York State Pathological Laboratory, the first laboratory in the world to be devoted solely to the study of cancer. Courtesy History of Medicine Collection.

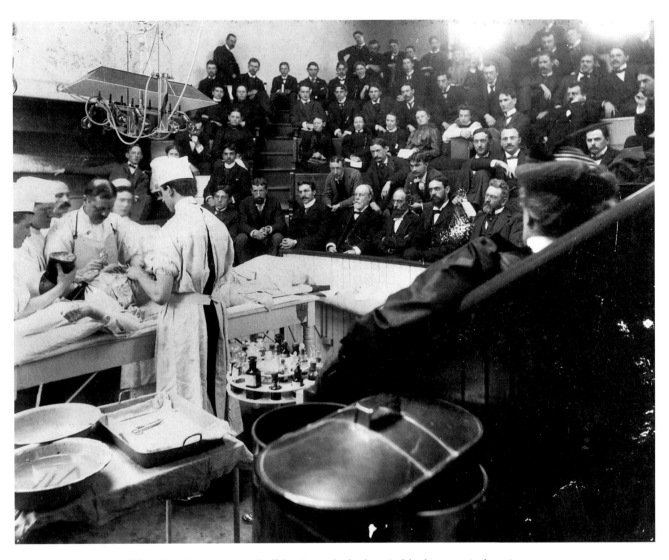

When Dr. Park came to Buffalo General, the hospital had no surgical equipment at all and during his first year in the city he had to carry the instruments he needed to use at the hospital from home every day. Here medical students observe him circa 1898. The original sepia tone photo belonged to Dr. Floyd Spaulding, Class of 1898. Courtesy University Archives.

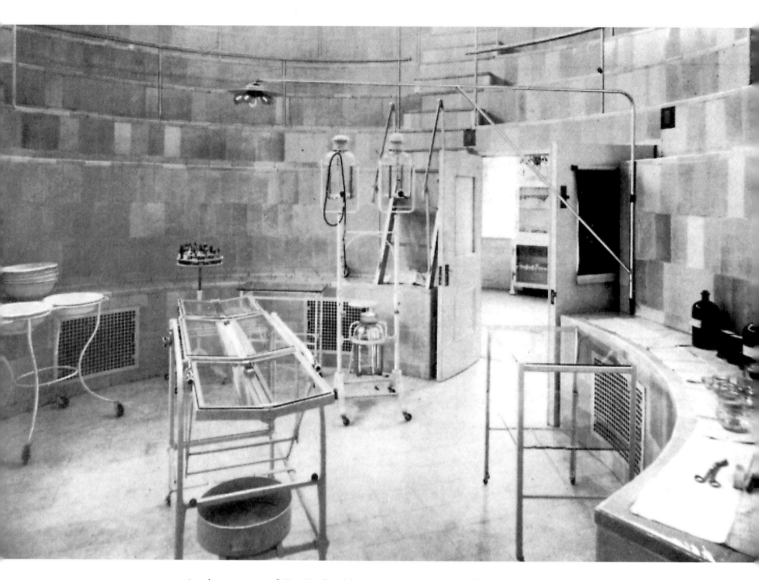

At the request of Dr. Park, this surgical theater was built at Buffalo General Hospital and equipped with the latest technology. Courtesy Buffalo General Hospital Archives.

Dr. Park died in 1914 at the age of 62. His death mask was made by Dr. Charles R. Bethune, Class of 1905. In nineteen scrapbooks now held in the University Archives, Dr. Park documented his professional career. Dr. Park was a multifaceted man and his interests covered a broad spectrum of professional, philosophic, aesthetic, and political subjects. A surgeon of consummate skill and an eminent teacher, he was the author of numerous scientific papers and books, including a textbook on general surgery. He was an early advocate of antisepsis and asepsis and the first director of the cancer research institute that now bears his name. He is credited with teaching the first formal course in the history of medicine in this country and publishing a text on medical history based on his lectures. Courtesy History of Medicine Collection.

Above: When the forty-eighth session of the Medical School commenced on September 25, 1893, the School had moved to 24 High Street near the Buffalo General Hospital. The new building was so tastefully designed and well built that it was considered to be one of the most attractive buildings of any kind outside New York City. Finished with terra cotta, pressed brick, iron, and hard wood, it contained three amphitheaters, a chemical laboratory, a dissecting room beautifully lighted and ventilated, and a magnificent library of 4,000 volumes. Courtesy History of Medicine Collection.

Facing page: Designed by George Cary, the new Medical School building was completed at a cost of $150,000 and, according to the Annual Circular or school catalog, it was the best arranged medical college edifice in the United States, perhaps even the world. Professors could drive their carriages directly into the elegant entrance hall of the School, allowing them to enter the building without being exposed to inclement weather. The building was modeled after the Palazzo Farnese in Rome and the lanterns were made by craftsmen in Florence. Today, one of the lanterns hangs in Farber Hall on the South Campus, while the other is in private hands. Courtesy History of Medicine Collection.

Pictured above is the medical library at 24 High Street. In 1847, the Annual Circular noted a library of 519 volumes purchased at a cost of $829.96. James Platt White formed a library committee of one and, when necessary, supplemented the library holdings with works from his father's collection. On his death, Dr. White left his medical library of more than 1,000 volumes to the School of Medicine. In addition to the James Platt White donation, the library has been the recipient of some of the most noteworthy collections in Western New York, including those of Dr. George Burwell, a prominent nineteenth-century local physician, and Dr. Roswell Park. Courtesy History of Medicine Collection.

The main amphitheater, named Alumni Hall in recognition of contributions toward equipment and furnishings made by graduates of the School, had a seating capacity of four hundred. Additional courses were added to the curriculum and new teaching methods were employed, including recitation courses that forced students to come to class better prepared. The original faculty of seven had increased to almost fifty by 1893, including a large number of adjunct faculty. Clinical instruction improved and an outpatient department was established within the Medical School building. Courtesy History of Medicine Collection.

Lectures in anatomy and pathology were illustrated using skeletons, diagrams, models, mannequins, and pathological specimens. The skeletons of the man, horse, and dog shown above were later donated to the Buffalo Museum of Science, while some of the other artifacts are held by the Medical School. Courtesy History of Medicine Collection.

Charles Cary (1852–1931), Class of 1875, worked untiringly to raise funds for the Medical School. It was largely through his efforts that the new building was made possible. His brother, George Cary, was the architect. Dr. Cary was also instrumental in securing the funding for the New York State Pathological Laboratory. He taught at the Medical School for thirty-two years and served as dean before becoming emeritus professor in 1911. Cary Hall in the present Medical School complex is named in recognition of the contributions of the Carys, a distinguished Buffalo family. Courtesy History of Medicine Collection.

Facing page, bottom: In 1887 and 1892, respectively, the Schools of Law and Dentistry were added. Dentistry was also located in the Medical School on High Street until a separate dental building was constructed on 25 Goodrich Street. This interior photo shows the bare brick walls of the dental clinic. The Law School, founded in 1887 under the sponsorship of Niagara University, was incorporated into the University in 1891. Courtesy University Archives.

Although the founding faculty had intended to establish a full university, the Medical School remained the only department until 1886 when the School of Pharmacy was organized. The Pharmacy School was located in the Medical School building at Main and Virginia and moved with the Medical School to the new quarters on 24 High Street. Pictured here is the pharmacognosy laboratory on High Street. Courtesy University Archives.

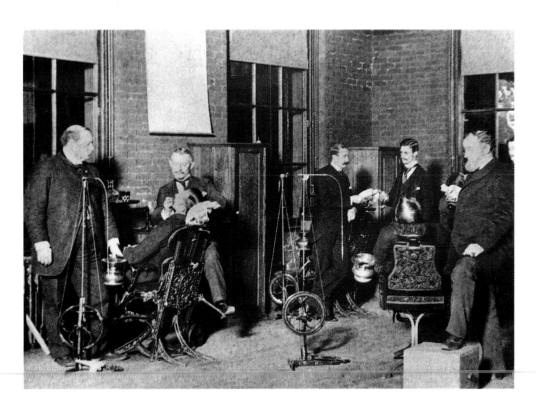

Although Niagara University never attracted as many medical students as did the University of Buffalo, it helped raise the standards of medical education in Buffalo. Niagara University's faculty included many of the city's most prominent practitioners, including Henry C. Buswell, who, according to William Osler, was one of the country's foremost diagnosticians, and Alvin Hubbell, nationally known ophthalmologist and medical historian. By the mid-1890s, however, it had become increasingly clear that Buffalo was not large enough to sustain two medical schools; they merged in 1898. The graduates of Niagara University, including the Class of 1895 shown here, were considered alumni of the University of Buffalo. Many of the faculty members at Niagara University received appointments at the University. Courtesy University Archives.

Some of the graduates of the University of Buffalo's Medical School, Class of
1904, are shown here. Courtesy University Archives.

The Pan American Exposition, delayed by the Spanish-American War, opened in Buffalo on May 1, 1901, on a large tract of land next to the lake in Delaware Park. The Buffalo and Erie County Historical Society was the only permanent building to be constructed, but a number of magnificent temporary structures were erected. The Albright-Knox Art Gallery, originally intended as one of the permanent buildings, was not completed until 1905. Courtesy Buffalo and Erie County Historical Society.

President William McKinley regarded large expositions as the timekeepers of progress, and a visit by him to Buffalo had been scheduled. On September 5, 1901, designated as the exposition's President's Day, attendance broke all records. The following day a public reception was held in the Temple of Music. President McKinley, who prided himself on a "50-a-minute" handshake, was shot twice in the abdomen while standing in the receiving line. The assailant, Leon F. Czolgosz, a self-declared anarchist, was quickly subdued. He was declared legally sane, tried, and executed seven weeks later. A group of three eminent psychiatrists from Buffalo had doubted his sanity, but never were called at the trial, possibly on the theory that "mad or not, he should die." After his burial, two distinguished Boston physicians disclosed that Czolgosz had suffered a severe mental depression three years earlier. Courtesy History of Medicine Collection.

The president was carried on a stretcher to this ambulance and driven to the Emergency Hospital on the exposition grounds. Straw was wrapped around the tires to provide a smoother ride. The first surgeon to reach the president was Dr. Herman Mynter. He found that one bullet had been deflected by a button and left only a graze on the skin. The other had entered the left upper quadrant of the abdomen. Courtesy Buffalo General Hospital Archives.

Intended to treat emergencies, the Emergency Hospital, located at the Elmwood Avenue entrance to the fair grounds, had been organized by Roswell Park. Keeping in mind the fire that had occurred at the World's Fair in Chicago, as well as medical emergencies at other expositions, Dr. Park recommended building a small, but convenient structure. The upper floor contained rooms for the superintendent and half a dozen nurses, while the first floor was equipped as a hospital. At the close of the exposition, 5,400 individuals had been treated there. Courtesy History of Medicine Collection.

The Emergency Hospital was served by a house staff of recent graduates of the Medical School, one of whom was always on duty, and by half a dozen nurses. In addition to Dr. Park, back row, right, there was also a deputy medical director. When the president was shot, Dr. Park was in Niagara Falls performing an operation on a patient with a malignant lymphoma of the neck. A surgeon assisting Dr. Park in Niagara Falls related that halfway through the operation a messenger burst into the operating room and said, "Dr. Park, you are wanted at once in Buffalo." When Dr. Park answered that he could not leave this case even if it were for the president of the United States, the messenger answered: "Doctor, it is for the president of the United States." Courtesy Buffalo General Hospital Archives.

61

Since Dr. Park was unavailable, Matthew D. Mann was chosen to perform the operation. He was assisted by other local surgeons, and the president's personal physician, P. M. Rixey, was also present. A graduate of Yale College and the College of Physicians and Surgeons in New York, Dr. Mann was well trained in this country and abroad and he was at the height of his career. However, his specialty was obstetrics and gynecology, and he had never operated on a gunshot wound. Nevertheless, the physicians present all agreed that the operation should be performed as soon as possible. Courtesy History of Medicine Collection.

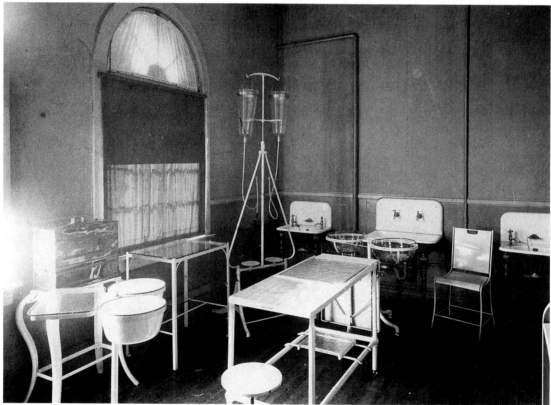

The operating room was equipped to treat minor injuries, not to perform major surgery. Dr. Mann used the instruments available. Unfortunately, he was not aware that Dr. Park's surgical case had been fetched from his home and was in an adjacent room. Another handicap was lighting. The operation began at 5:20 P.M. and, as the sun began to set, the windows did not let in enough light. The president's personal physician, Dr. Rixey, directed the fading sunlight into the incision with a mirror and later helped rig up an electric light. Courtesy Buffalo General Hospital Archives.

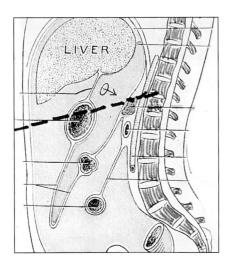

The bullet had perforated both front and back walls of the stomach, taking off a tip of the pancreas as it tore through the portly president. The bullet lay out of reach somewhere in the paraspinal musculature. During the operation, both entrance and exit wounds in the stomach were closed and the peritoneal cavity irrigated. Dr. Mynter recommended that a drain be inserted, but Dr. Mann did not believe it necessary. This decision would later be criticized. Toward the end of the operation, Dr. Park arrived from Niagara Falls and concurred that further exploration to retrieve the bullet was too dangerous in view of the president's weakened condition. The operation lasted ninety-one minutes and the patient was subsequently transferred to a private home. Courtesy University at Buffalo Publications Department.

The president rallied and most of the official bulletins over the next few days remained optimistic. Members of his family and cabinet as well as Dr. Charles McBurney of New York City, who had been called in as a special consultant, had departed from Buffalo. On September 13, the president's condition worsened. His pulse became rapid and less forceful and he developed a slight fever. He died the following morning. The official cause of death was severe gangrene of the retroperitoneum, an acceptable diagnosis in that day. Although the official announcement of the president's death showed unanimity among his physicians, criticism of the handling of the president's care has continued to this day. On September 14, 1901, Theodore Roosevelt was sworn in as president of the United States. No photos were taken of the event, which took place in the library of the Wilcox mansion on Delaware Avenue. The mansion is now a national historic site. Courtesy Buffalo and Erie County Historical Society.

The hopes and disappointments of the constant dream of a total University of Buffalo are reflected in this cartoon from the University yearbook, the *Iris*, of 1906. Within a decade, the "mirage" was a reality. Courtesy University Archives.

Chapter 4

Educational Reform and World War I

From the very beginning the founding fathers harbored dreams of a greater University, embracing an undergraduate college of arts and sciences as well as professional schools. The issue of undergraduate education recurred sporadically through the years, and a serious effort was launched again in 1905. This initiative enjoyed such public support that in 1909 the County of Erie sold 106 acres of the present South Campus, valued at between $200,000 and $300,000, to the University for $54,300, subject only to the University's pledge to devote the property to University uses within ten years. However, two years later a resolution for City of Buffalo funding for the undergraduate college was unexpectedly defeated by a groundswell of ethnic, religious, political and professional opposition.

The dream of becoming a total university was strangely kept alive from another quarter: the Flexner Report. In 1908, the Carnegie Foundation for the Advancement of Teaching commissioned a critical examination of the 155 medical schools in the United States and Canada, under the direction of Abraham Flexner, a renowned educator. His report was a scathing indictment of American medical education. Dr. Flexner recommended reduction of the 155 schools to 31, and the Buffalo Medical School was not among the chosen. In response to Flexner's report, the American Medical Association decreed in 1913 that to retain Class A accreditation status, medical schools must require entering students to have completed at least one year of college. In September of that year (1913), the University offered the first year of a program of "Courses in Arts and Sciences." Twenty-six of the sixty-two students enrolled in the first semester were classified as premed.

BUFFALO: *Population, 401,441.*

(3) UNIVERSITY OF BUFFALO MEDICAL DEPARTMENT. Organized 1846. Despite the university charter, the University of Buffalo is a fiction. Schools of medicine, law, dentistry, and pharmacy are aggregated under the designation; but they are to all intents and purposes independent schools, each living on its own fees.

Entrance requirement: Admission is on the basis of the Regents' Medical Student Certificate, being the equivalent of a high school education.

Attendance: 193.

Teaching staff: 97, of whom 38 are professors.

Resources available for maintenance: Fees amounting to $31,984.

Laboratory facilities: The school has a conventionally adequate equipment for anatomy, ordinary laboratories for chemistry, bacteriology, and pathology, a meager outfit in physiology,—it having been found that the students cannot profitably do much experimental work themselves,—nothing for pharmacology. The "whole-time" teachers have in the main other duties besides teaching in medicine: the professor of pathology and bacteriology is registrar, the chemist officiates in the pharmacy department, the anatomist in the dental department. There is a small museum, but a good library of 8000 volumes, current German and English periodicals, with a librarian in charge.

Clinical facilities: For clinical teaching, the school relies mainly on the Buffalo General Hospital close by. It has access to some 200 beds, used for demonstrative teaching in the wards. Records are made by internes. Students do no clinical laboratory work in connection with special patients, the teaching in clinical microscopy being separately given at the college. Infectious diseases are didactically taught. Clinical obstetrics is imperfectly organized. Besides the Buffalo General Hospital, a weekly clinic is held at the County Hospital, four miles distant, four clinics at the Sisters' Hospital, one and a half miles away, etc.

Despite the size of the city, the college dispensary is wretched. It has an attendance of perhaps 3000 during the college year, skin, eye, and ear cases mainly. A definite statement is impossible because there are no systematic records. The rooms are ill equipped. Records consist of brief pencil notes in separate books, usually without index. The work is hastily and superficially done, and its influence on the students, so far as it goes, must be thoroughly bad. The catalogue states, however, that as attendance in the dispensary is obligatory, each student "will secure an unusually thorough training in the taking and recording of histories."

Date of visit: October, 1909.

Abraham Flexner advocated a European model of medical education: a medical school within a larger university, with a teaching hospital attached to the school and adequate and separate endowment support. He therefore disparaged proprietary schools sustained by fees alone (like Buffalo's) and critically questioned the distribution of fee income ("dividends") to leading faculty practitioners of the town who needed it least, rather than applying it to the maintenance and improvement of clinical and laboratory facilities. He was also adamant about high standards for admission to medical school, in keeping with his support of university-affiliated medical schools. Reproduced here is his report on the Buffalo Medical School.

Plans for expanding these courses into a College of Arts and Sciences were sustained in 1915 when property and a building—Townsend Hall—to house a full-scale liberal arts college were donated to the University by the Women's Educational and Industrial Union of Buffalo. This gift, too, was contingent, this time upon the University raising an endowment of $100,000. Within a year, the required endowment was raised, thanks in large measure to a gift from Grace Knox, a prominent citizen. With gifts and pledges from members of the Knox family and from General Edmund Hayes, a civic leader, and others, the future of the College of Arts and Sciences was assured. In 1920 the first four-year bachelor's degrees were conferred.

When the United States entered World War I, many members of Buffalo's medical community enlisted. Buffalonians manned the U.S. Army Base Hospital Twenty-three in Vittel, France, a large field hospital complex mobilized by the Red Cross. It serviced almost 15,000 patients during the war. Those who stayed behind fought an even more powerful enemy: influenza. This great epidemic occurred in 1918. Strict public health measures were imposed in Buffalo. The city suffered only slightly more than half the morbidity rate of the nation at large.

Development of medical technology and research and the growth of specialization were to characterize the post-World War I years. The Medical School entered the second decade of the twentieth century stronger for having survived the recommendation of closure and for having its own preparatory undergraduate college.

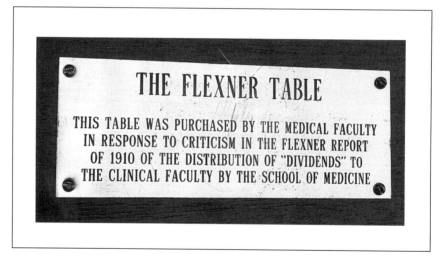

THE FLEXNER TABLE

THIS TABLE WAS PURCHASED BY THE MEDICAL FACULTY
IN RESPONSE TO CRITICISM IN THE FLEXNER REPORT
OF 1910 OF THE DISTRIBUTION OF "DIVIDENDS" TO
THE CLINICAL FACULTY BY THE SCHOOL OF MEDICINE

In response to the criticism, the Medical School faculty donated to the School a splendid mahogany Kittinger conference table. It is inscribed with the explanatory plaque pictured here. The table is in regular use in the Dean's Office and is a fitting tribute to the further development and proud survival of the School of Medicine. Photos by James A. Ulrich, University Academic Services/Computing and Information Technology.

Townsend Hall, located on Niagara Square, was the first home of the undergraduate College of Arts and Sciences. The building was named after Mrs. Harriet A. Townsend, the first president of the Women's Educational and Industrial Union of Buffalo, a group that helped women find fair treatment in schools and in the workplace. The formal presentation of the building was made on University Day, February 22, 1915. Courtesy University Archives.

Pictured here is the office of the College of Arts and Sciences in Townsend Hall, 1916. Courtesy University Archives.

ONE FOURTH YEAR STUDENT
VACCINATING ANOTHER

By the turn of the twentieth century, widespread vaccination against contagious diseases had been established. Here, in 1912, students are practicing on one another. Public health principles assumed increasing importance in medical practice and education, as did industrial medicine, laboratory and clinical research, and the rapid dissemination of research and clinical data. Courtesy University Archives.

Asepsis was also a critical aspect of medical care and medical education. The importance of cleanliness was championed by Semmelweiss, Lister, and, in America, by Oliver Wendell Holmes in the latter part of the nineteenth century. Students learn the technique of "scrubbing" in this 1912 photo. Courtesy University Archives.

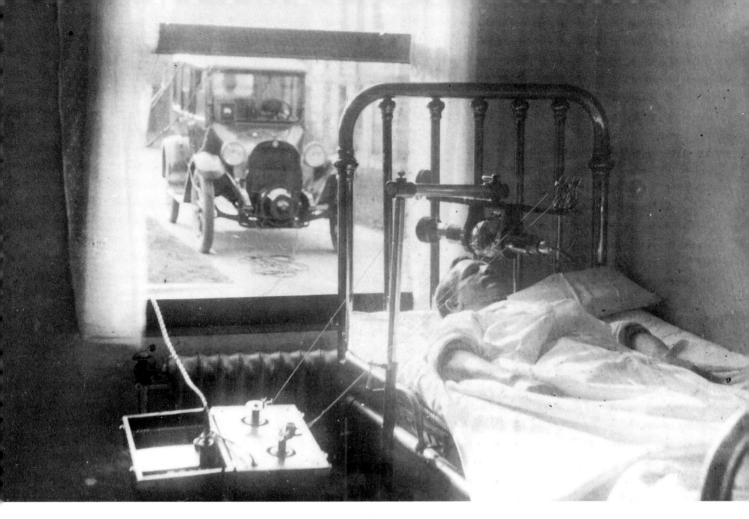

House calls were made with a portable x-ray machine, this one from the Deaconess Hospital, around 1911. It was powered by the crank-generator on the doctor's car because at this time few Buffalo homes were wired for electricity. Courtesy Buffalo General Hospital Archives.

Concern was focused as well on the sterilization of instruments. This photo from about 1914 shows a boiler, far left, equipment for cold chemicals in the center, and an autoclave for sterilization by steam under pressure, far right. Courtesy University Archives.

Charles William Eustace   Carlton Lakey Vanderboget   Julius James Klein   Clyde Lorenzo Carey   James Macpherson McColl

Frederick Edward Sperry   Roy A. Paxton   August Howard Stein   James Cornelius Sullivan   Clayton Wellington Green   Otto Ignatius Rebescher   Frederick William Baeslack

lias Khalil Fakhoury   Frank Victor Hoehn   James Walter Grenolds   James Henry Stygall   Leslie Mayo Wilkins   William Stephen Hartigan   Marion Alvah Keyes, Jr.   Roy John Juhre   Frederick Ettore Strozzi   George J. Saylin

Stanley John Brown   Charles Ellsworth Goodell   Nadina Reinstein Kavinosky   Jennie Harper Harris   Raymond William Stockwell   Nellie Ettie Kurtz   Clarence Clark Nesbitt   Albert Warren Wagner   Benedict James Duffy

Thomas Joseph Burke   Howard Andrew Orvis   Michael James McMahon   Anthony Stanislaus Culkowski   Ralph Raymond Hughes   Raymond Joseph Blum   John Vincent Hogan

CLASS OF 1910
MEDICAL DEPARTMENT UNIVERSITY OF BUFFALO, N. Y.

The Class of 1910 poses for a graduation photo. Courtesy University Archives.

An Alumni Association of the Medical School was formed in 1875. The earliest existing picture is this one photographed at the group's forty-second annual meeting held from May 31 to June 2, 1917, at the School on High Street. Courtesy University Archives.

The James A. Gibson Anatomical Society was formed by the Medical School Classes of 1919 and 1920 as a tribute to the memory of the professor who taught anatomy at the Medical School from 1894 until he died in 1917. The society that bears his name, still active today, was formed to promote interest in anatomical study and research and to honor students proficient in these areas. Courtesy History of Medicine Collection.

When the United States entered World War I, some Medical School students left school to enlist in the military. Others did their part in the Liberty Loan and Red Cross campaigns, or joined the Enlisted Medical Reserve Corps or the Naval Reserves. Pictured here are members of the University Band patriotically marching past the High Street building. Courtesy University Archives.

U.S. Army Base Hospital Twenty-three was mobilized in August 1917. Medical personnel left Buffalo on November 21, 1917, to staff the hospital and reached Vittel on December 19 (shown here detraining). Vittel was a fashionable tourist town, world-famed for the medicinal properties of its curative waters, with a gambling casino, race courses, golf courses, tennis courts and many hotels. The Twenty-third Unit took over seven of the hotels and used them as hospitals with a capacity to treat more than 3,000 patients. Courtesy Buffalo General Hospital Archives.

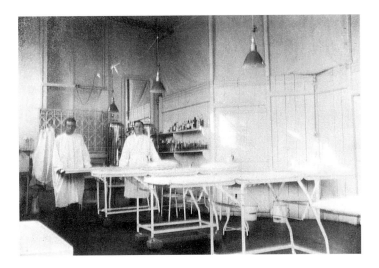

This operating room was located in the surgical hospital, formerly the elegant Terminus Hotel. The operating rooms were busy night and day. Base Hospital Twenty-three operated as an evacuation unit, and patients were moved as quickly as possible to hospitals farther from the front lines. Locations as close as ten miles away were bombed, but Base Hospital Twenty-three was never hit. Of the 172 deaths recorded at the hospital, 83 were from disease, 84 from wounds, and 5 from gas infection. Courtesy Buffalo General Hospital Archives.

The funeral cortege of Captain Lorenzo Burrows winds through the streets of Vittel. Dr. Burrows, an ophthalmologist, was the beloved adjutant of Base Hospital Twenty-three. He died September 17, 1918, of pneumonia following influenza, the first fatality of the unit staff. A nurse and four enlisted men died in the same epidemic. Courtesy Buffalo General Hospital Archives.

Another march through the streets of Vittel, this time homeward bound. U.S. Army Base Hospital Twenty-three left Vittel in March 1919. Courtesy Buffalo General Hospital Archives.

Dr. M. Louise Hurrell, Class of 1902, spent 1918–19 as director of the American Women's Hospital, Unit One, at Luzancy, France. There she and her all-female staff administered care to 20,000 patients at the cost of less than one dollar per patient. She practiced most of her life in Rochester. Courtesy History of Medicine Collection.

Francis E. Fronczak, Class of 1897, is shown in his uniform as officer in the U.S. Medical Corps, 1917. In addition to his medical degree, he received a law degree from the University in 1900. He gained an international reputation aiding the people of Poland during World Wars I and II. Dr. Fronczak was recognized as one of the foremost authorities on public health. From 1910 to 1946 he was associate professor of hygiene and preventive medicine, then received the title of emeritus associate professor. Fronczak Hall, on the North Campus, is named for him. Courtesy Francis E. Fronczak Collection, Butler Library, Buffalo State College.

Left: While medical students for the most part were spared the horrors of war, many faculty and alumni served. On April 1, 1919, returning veterans were welcomed home as they paraded up Main Street past the Buffalo Savings Bank building. In 1920, most of the alumni from the classes of 1918 and 1919 were still in the military, so the director of the Erie County Hospital used junior and senior medical students as interns. Courtesy Buffalo and Erie County Historical Society.

Wende Hall, a building on the South Campus, was named in honor of Grover William Wende. Dr. Wende, Class of 1889, a much-loved Buffalo physician, was one of the leading dermatologists in the nation. He noted many rare diseases, including a description of nodular tuberculosis of the skin. He was one of the most skillful dermatologic photographers in the country. Courtesy University Archives.

Dr. Ernest Wende, Grover Wende's older brother, invented the modern nipple for baby bottles, like these advertised in the 1913 *Medic.* Easier to clean than the nipple-and-tube contraption of earlier years, it helped prevent milk-borne infections in infants. A member of the Class of 1878, he was one of the most outstanding health officers in the country. Courtesy University Archives.

Fighting a Deadlier Foe: Influenza

While the World War raged on in Europe, many Americans were fighting a more powerful enemy: influenza. The U.S. death toll for the war was 116,516, but the influenza epidemic of 1918–1919 killed 550,000 Americans. Worldwide, influenza killed 20 million people. Only the Bubonic Plague of 540–558 A.D. and the Black Death of the fourteenth century were deadlier. Buffalo weathered the epidemic better than most cities because of the leadership provided by the Medical School and its alumni.

Facing Page: Buffalo physicians garbed to reduce the risk of contagion. The acting health commissioner, Dr. Franklin C. Gram, Class of 1891, formed a special advisory committee to deal with the epidemic. Its membership included Dr. Walter S. Goodale, Class of 1903, who later would chair the Department of Hygiene and Public Health. Hospitals were asked to dedicate half their beds to influenza cases, and Buffalo's Central High School (today Hutchinson Central Technical School) was converted into a temporary hospital. The greatest need, however, was manpower. On October 16, 1918, the senior class of the Medical School was pressed into service, and the next day the order was extended to include members of the junior and sophomore classes. Courtesy Buffalo and Erie County Historical Society.

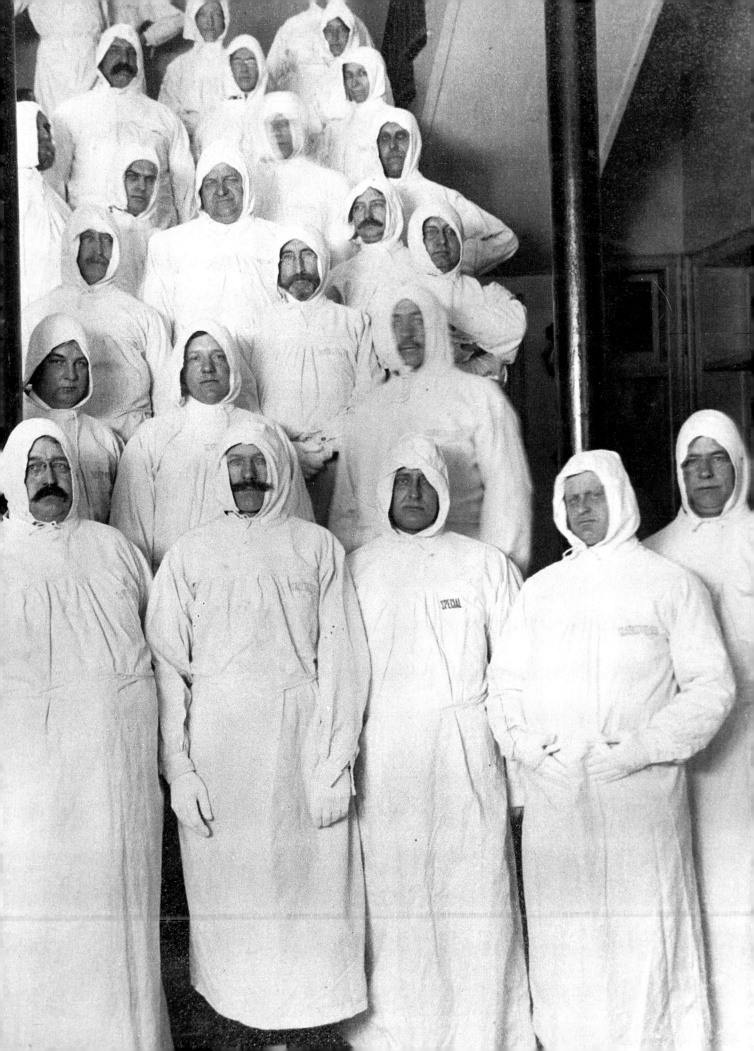

Though citizens complained, on October 10 the acting health commissioner imposed draconian measures that virtually shut the city down for weeks. Public assembly of more than ten people was prohibited. This included streetcars, theaters, movies, schools, saloons, and church services, even funerals. With the exception of military courses, the University canceled all classes and prohibited football games with out-of-town schools. Reprinted from *Buffalo Physician and Biomedical Scientist.*

Even ordinary citizens wore gauze masks. Buffalo had been a prime target for influenza. Its large population of immigrants was particularly vulnerable, and troops moving through the city helped spread the disease. There was no treatment; doctors could only try to make the patient comfortable and stem the spread. Within a month of the outbreak, it appeared that Buffalo's strict public health measures had worked. Buffalo suffered only a 6 percent morbidity rate, compared to 10 percent nationwide. Reprinted from *Buffalo Physician and Biomedical Scientist.*

Buffalo Homeopathic Hospital, shown here at Cottage and Maryland Streets, was founded in 1872. Homeopathic medicine, developed in Germany in the early nineteenth century in reaction to the harsh therapeutics of heroic medicine, was based on the tenet that diseases could be cured by administering minute doses of drugs which, if given in large amounts, would produce the symptoms of a disease. Since homeopathic physicians were often barred from practicing at regular hospitals, they started their own institutions. The Buffalo Homeopathic Hospital was restricted to the practice of homeopathy until 1923 when regular physicians were permitted to join the staff. That same year the name was changed to the Millard Fillmore Hospital. Courtesy Buffalo and Erie County Historical Society.

Chapter 5

Development of the Hospitals

Prior to the Civil War, American hospitals were mainly places to care for the poor, destitute, and homeless. There was relatively little that medicine could do to cure people, so most patients who had a home elected to stay there, as friends and relatives provided better care.

In 1873, the United States had only 178 hospitals, but by the early twentieth century the number increased to more than 4,000. The hospital became the center of modern medical practice for several reasons. Anesthesia and asepsis had turned surgery into commonplace treatment for many conditions, x-ray technology required special facilities, and advances in biochemistry made a fully equipped laboratory necessary for diagnostic tests and treatment. Florence Nightingale's contributions to hospital sanitation and architecture were also important factors.

In Buffalo, new hospitals and numerous smaller clinics were established between 1870 and 1920. Competition among regular, homeopathic, and eclectic physicians intensified, culminating in the founding of the Buffalo Homeopathic Hospital and Pierce's Invalids' Hotel. Ethnic and religious groups started their own hospitals, some of which have become affiliated with the Medical School while others have since closed or consolidated. To meet the demand for professional nurses, Sisters Hospital, Buffalo General Hospital, Buffalo Homeopathic Hospital, and Children's Hospital all started their own nursing schools in the late nineteenth century.

In 1967, plans were announced to construct a University hospital on the Amherst Campus, but these plans never materialized. Today, the Medical School relies on a network of affiliated hospitals to provide clinical training. These hospitals are expanding in new directions, opening satellite facilities that offer primary care services, skilled nursing beds, specialized care, or laboratory services. The Medical School and the affiliated hospitals have also formed two highly successful consortia to coordinate graduate medical programs and avoid duplication of services.

The first nursing school west of New York City was founded at Buffalo General Hospital in 1877. This photo shows nursing graduates from the Buffalo Homeopathic Hospital, which started its nursing school ten years later. The first Visiting Nurses Association in the country was established in Buffalo in 1885 in response to the need for health care of an expanding population, including many immigrants. Courtesy Buffalo and Erie County Historical Society.

Buffalo General Hospital comprised several buildings circa 1910. From right are the medical and surgical ward, clinic, administration, and private rooms. In the rear left is the nurses' home, and behind that, the Harrington Children's Hospital or ward. Courtesy Buffalo General Hospital Archives.

In 1876, Dr. Ray Vaughn Pierce, an eclectic physician-entrepreneur, founded a hospital in Buffalo. Until his death in 1914, he competed successfully with the regular medical establishment for patients. In contrast to the Spartan wards of regular hospitals, the private rooms in the Invalids' Hotel (also named the Palace Hotel) had fireplaces, fifteen-foot ceilings, Brussels carpets, and many other luxuries. Dr. Pierce provided not only specialized ambulatory and surgical services, but also conducted a large mail order business in patent medicines. Courtesy Buffalo and Erie County Historical Society.

James Platt White, one of the founders of the Medical School, was instrumental in establishing the Buffalo State Hospital. Although a movement to open a state hospital for the insane in Western New York began as early as 1869, it was not until 1880 that the hospital was ready to receive patients. Located on Forest Avenue, the splendid building was designed by the architect Henry Hobson Richardson according to the latest theories about the care and treatment of the insane. Courtesy History of Medicine Collection.

Facing page, top: The Buffalo Eye and Ear Infirmary was established in 1876 by Lucian Howe, the School's first professor of ophthalmology. He became known as the father of the "Howe law," passed by New York State in 1896, which required that the eyes of newborns be treated with diluted silver nitrate to prevent blindness. He was a prolific author and endowed a prize given by the Medical Society in the State of New York for medical investigation, especially in the field of ophthalmology. In 1926, Dr. Howe left Buffalo for Harvard University where he endowed and developed the Howe Ophthalmology Laboratories. The name of the Buffalo infirmary was later changed to the Wettlaufer Clinic and eventually merged with the Deaconess Hospital. Today the clinic is located in the Buffalo General Hospital. Courtesy Joseph F. Monte, M.D.

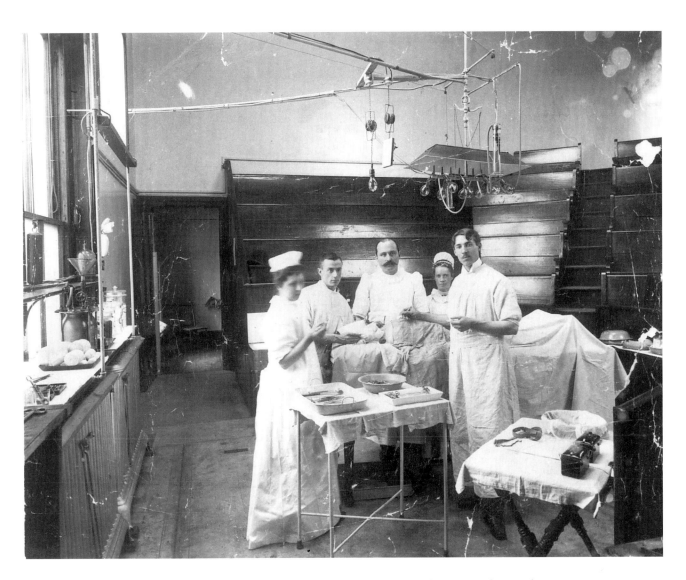

This 1883 photo shows Matthew D. Mann, professor of obstetrics and gynecology, at right, performing surgery in the first operating room in Buffalo equipped with electric lights. Buffalo General Hospital was one of the first buildings in town to be electrified. Courtesy Buffalo General Hospital Archives.

Sisters Hospital is shown here in a photo from 1890 when it was located on Main and Delavan. Courtesy Buffalo and Erie County Historical Society.

Sisters Hospital was the first in Buffalo to establish an ambulance service. In 1884, the hospital opened the Emergency Hospital, a branch that treated mainly industrial accidents. Patients requiring more extensive care were transferred to Sisters Hospital in this two-horse-powered ambulance. Courtesy Sisters Hospital Archives.

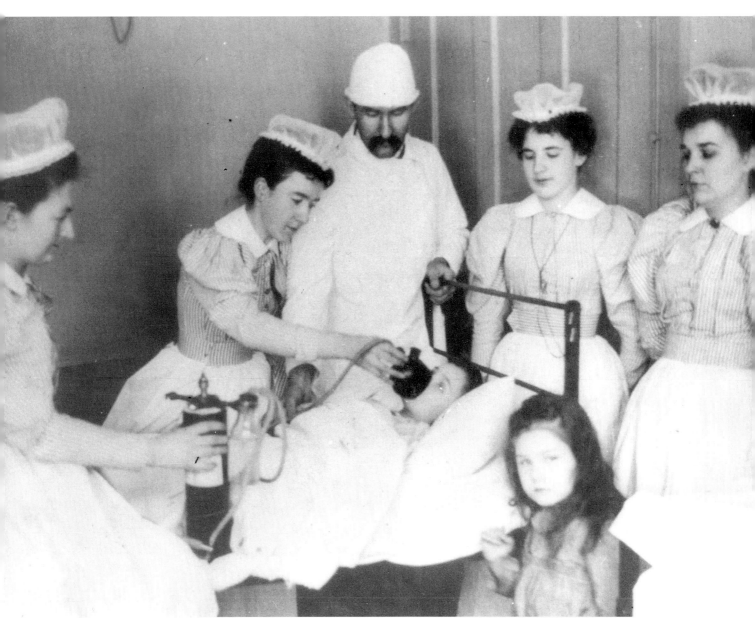

A nurse administers oxygen to a child in 1895 at Buffalo General Hospital.
Courtesy Buffalo and Erie County Historical Society.

The original German Deaconess Hospital, founded in 1896, had 120 beds: forty for patients, forty for the elderly, and forty for the deaconesses. When New York State mandated that a University family practice residency be instituted, the program developed at Deaconess Hospital eventually became the University's Department of Family Medicine in 1969. This is but one example of the significant role played by many local hospitals in the history of the Medical School. Courtesy Buffalo General Hospital Archives.

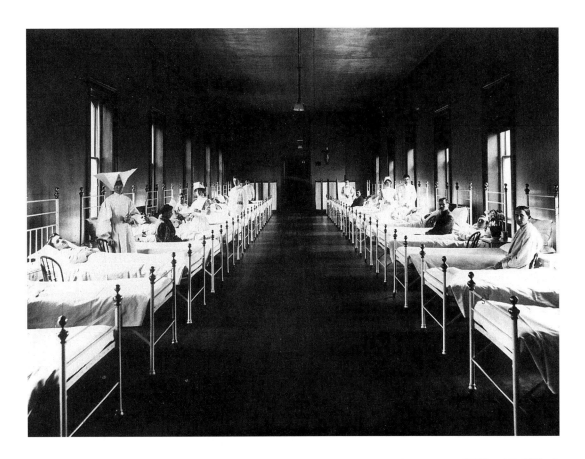

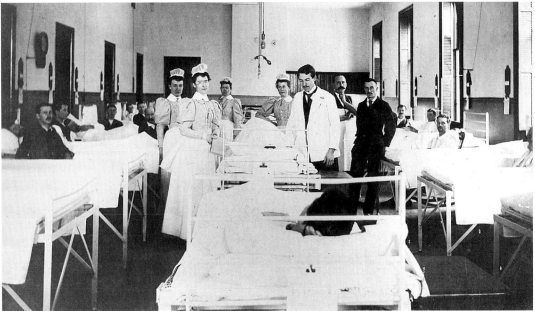

Top: This photo from 1897 shows a large ward at Sisters Hospital which, at that time, was the teaching hospital of Niagara University Medical School. Courtesy Sisters Hospital Archives.

Bottom: Doctors and medical students conduct rounds at Buffalo General Hospital in this photo from 1897. The ward was crowded and patients lacked privacy. Courtesy Buffalo General Hospital Archives.

Largely through the efforts of Roswell Park and Edward H. Butler, publisher of the *Buffalo Evening News*, the New York State Pathological Laboratory of the University of Buffalo was established in 1898. Funded by a state appropriation, it was the first laboratory in the world to be devoted solely to the study of cancer, and Dr. Park became its first director. During its formative years, the laboratory was located in the Medical School building on High Street. A separate building, shown in this photo, was constructed in 1901 and the institute was named for Mrs. William Gratwick who provided much of the funding for the new building. In 1911, the laboratory became a state institute and the name was changed to the New York State Institute for the Study of Malignant Diseases. In 1946, it was named in honor of its founder and first director. Courtesy History of Medicine Collection.

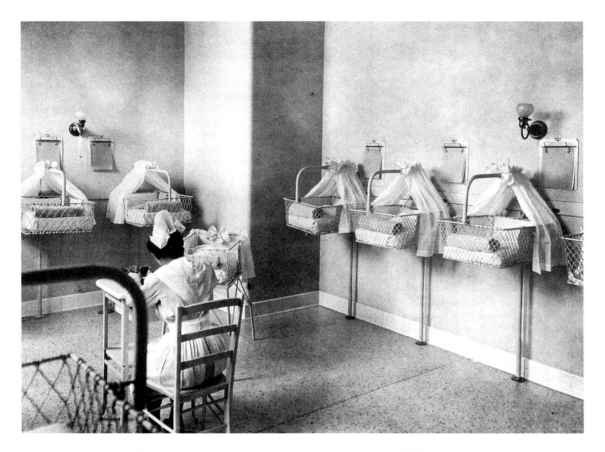

One of the oldest pediatric hospitals in the country, the Children's Hospital of Buffalo was founded in 1892. Although pediatrics had been taught in medical schools for fifty years, it was not until the turn of the century that effective treatment of childhood diseases became available. Children's Hospital greatly facilitated the development of the Department of Pediatrics at the University.

In this photo from 1922, bassinets line the walls of the nursery. The trend toward deliveries in hospitals rather than at home increased dramatically and, by 1939, more than 50 percent of all births occurred in hospitals. Courtesy Children's Hospital of Buffalo.

Mercy Hospital, founded by the Sisters of Mercy, opened in this house on Tifft Street in South Buffalo in 1904. The hospital had a capacity of thirty beds and cared mainly for the large Irish Catholic population of the city. During its first year of operation, the hospital installed an x-ray machine, established a school of nursing, and provided internships for medical school graduates. Courtesy Mercy Hospital.

The county had operated a hospital for the insane and an almhouse on the site of the present South Campus at Main and Bailey since mid-century. In 1093, a new law took effect that placed the care of the insane under state control, and the hospital building was left largely vacant. A group of physicians convinced the Board of Supervisors to establish a hospital, and in 1894, the Erie County Hospital opened. This photo shows interns and nursing staff in front of the new hospital in 1897. Courtesy University Archives.

The Consumption Annex of the Erie County Hospital was opened in 1895. It was built separately from the main structure based on the knowledge that consumption (tuberculosis) was an infectious disease. Great care was taken to provide comfort for the patients and the annex included billiard tables and other forms of entertainment. Courtesy History of Medicine Collection.

Left: Firefighters examine the charred remains of an annex after a fire damaged the Erie County Hospital at Main and Bailey in 1918. Courtesy Buffalo and Erie County Historical Society.

Right: Patients were comforted on the lawn of the County Hospital during the fire, then sent to the newly constructed Buffalo City Hospital on Grider Street. Courtesy Buffalo and Erie County Historical Society.

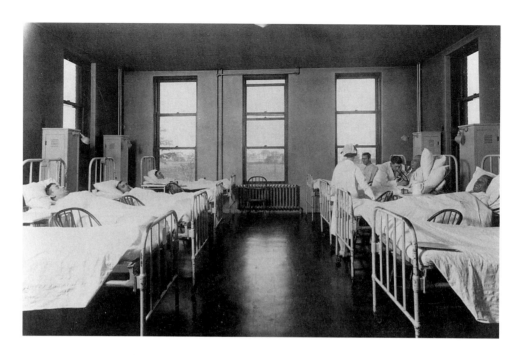

In response to the critical need for a larger facility to treat tuberculosis patients, the Common Council voted to establish the Buffalo City Hospital. The first building of the new hospital opened in 1918 on Grider Street. In 1939, it was named the Edward J. Meyer Memorial Hospital in honor of the physician who led the hospital from its founding until his death in 1935. Dr. Meyer, Class of 1891, was also responsible for the hospital's close affiliation with the Medical School. A second individual closely associated with the institution was Dr. Walter S. Goodale, Class of 1903, who served as administrator of the hospital for twenty-four years. In 1946, the hospital passed from city to county control and is now known as the Erie County Medical Center. Shown in this photo is the men's tubercular ward in the 1920s. Courtesy Erie County Medical Center.

Tonsillectomies were routine when this photo was taken in 1935 at Children's Hospital. A volunteer is on hand to amuse the group waiting for the operation. Courtesy Children's Hospital of Buffalo.

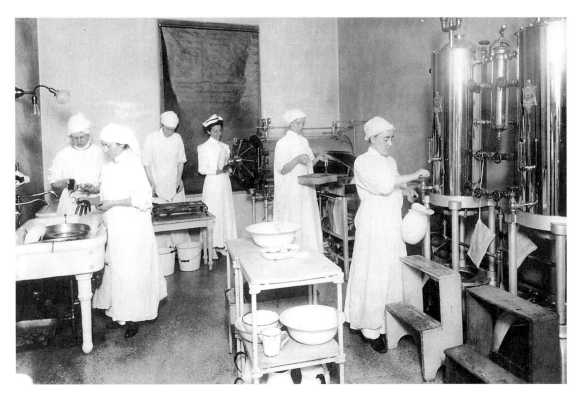

The importance of aseptic techniques is shown in this 1914 photo as nurses prepare rubber gloves and sterilize instruments before surgery at Deaconess Hospital. Courtesy Buffalo General Hospital Archives.

During the Great Depression, Dr. Walter S. Goodale developed an extensive home care service that included home deliveries by the staff of the Buffalo City Hospital (later called the Edward J. Meyer Memorial Hospital). Many physicians, unable to sustain their private practices, were employed by the hospital. Courtesy Buffalo and Erie County Historical Society.

This incubator from 1938 could be placed in an ambulance to rush a premature infant to a hospital. Children's Hospital set up its first incubators in 1902 after the staff saw the devices demonstrated at the Pan American Exposition the year before. Courtesy Children's Hospital of Buffalo.

Dr. Walter Murphy, director of radiation therapy, uses a Dictaphone to record his comments as he reads x-rays in the 1940s at what is now the Roswell Park Cancer Institute. Courtesy Roswell Park Cancer Institute.

In 1938, the Buffalo General Hospital house staff posed in the surgical amphitheater originally built for Dr. Roswell Park. The bas-relief frieze, a gift from the architect George Cary, was copied from a sixteenth-century Italian hospital. The Latin inscription translates: "In the presence of a sick man, let conversation cease, laughter be kept away, while the illness rules all." Courtesy Buffalo General Hospital Archives.

By 1950, no one would be allowed into the surgical theater wearing street clothes. Student observers were required to wear surgical garb, and a glass wall separated them from the patient. The disadvantage of observing from a distance in operating theaters is demonstrated by the resident resorting to binoculars in this photo taken at Buffalo General Hospital. Courtesy University Archives.

Children's Hospital, located on Bryant Street, is now a regional referral center for state-of-the-art pediatric medical and surgical specialties and a regional perinatal center. Courtesy Children's Hospital of Buffalo.

The 742-bed Buffalo General Hospital today delivers nearly 25 percent of all adult medical and surgical services in Erie County. In 1985, a sixteen-story medical tower was added to the hospital complex on High Street. The hospital is considered one of the most technologically advanced medical facilities in the northeast. Courtesy Buffalo General Hospital.

Today the Erie County Medical Center (ECMC) is well equipped to care for the most severely injured patients. The hospital is designated the regional center for adult trauma, adult burn treatment, spinal cord injury, and acute traumatic brain injury, as well as AIDS. It has 550 certified beds, 120 skilled nursing beds, and three off-site clinics. More than half of all the clinical departments of the Medical School are based at ECMC. Courtesy Erie County Medical Center.

Mercy Hospital is now a 483-bed community teaching hospital with an increasing emphasis on ambulatory care. Sponsored by the Sisters of Mercy and serving Buffalo and the Southtowns, the hospital operates several satellite facilities as well. Courtesy Mercy Hospital.

Today Millard Fillmore Health System operates two hospitals: a tertiary care hospital that includes a skilled nursing facility on Gates Circle, and a full-service suburban hospital on Maple Road in Amherst. Photo by James A. Ulrich, University Academic Services/Computing and Information Technology.

The Roswell Park Cancer Institute is designated a Comprehensive Cancer Center. A division of the New York State Department of Health, it is devoted to cancer research, treatment, and education. In addition to the clinical programs, the Roswell Park Graduate Division includes a program that works closely with the graduate school of the University and the basic science departments of the School of Medicine and Biomedical Sciences. Courtesy Roswell Park Cancer Institute.

Located at 2157 Main Street, Sisters Hospital today has 496 beds, including an eighty-bed skilled nursing facility, a coronary care unit, and an ambulatory care wing. Courtesy Sisters Hospital.

The dedication of the Veterans Administration Hospital was held in January 1950. For many years the city had attempted to have a veterans hospital located in Buffalo. In anticipation of the relocation of the Medical School to Main and Bailey, construction of the Veterans Hospital began on the Grover Cleveland Golf Course on Bailey Avenue. A 39,000-square-foot research building was constructed in 1990. In 1995, the hospital merged with VA facilities in Batavia and Rochester to form the Department of Veterans Affairs Western New York Health Care System. Courtesy Department of Veterans Affairs Western New York Health Care System.

Chapter 6

Student Life

"Rah-Re-Ri-Ro—
Ring-Ching-Chang—
1900 Medico—
Zip! Boom!! Bang!!!"
Class shout of the senior class of 1900

No history of the Medical School would be complete without a look at student life. Much of what we know comes from the yearbooks, first published in 1898, which chronicle the ebb and flow of student life. Some changes are obvious. Long flowing skirts for the women and starched collars for the men have been replaced with looser, more casual classroom attire. "Theater parties" are out; student follies are in. Fraternities and clubs come and go.

But beyond the reach of fashion and fad there remains one event that no student wants to miss: commencement, the ceremony that marks the joy and sense of accomplishment of becoming a doctor.

Left: A bicycling coed represented the new school spirit that was blossoming at the University at the turn of the century. Courtesy University Archives.

University Day was celebrated February 22, Washington's birthday, beginning in 1901, to promote school spirit. The men students from each school assembled at their respective buildings and marched in a body to a theater, where the ceremony included benediction, speeches, and music, followed by a luncheon and receptions. In 1917, the age of women's suffrage, the women students marched in the procession for the first time, waving pennants. Courtesy University Archives.

A drawing from the yearbook illustrates the "theater parties" at public plays that were popular with University students around the turn of the century. During the performance, students shouted comments and generally acted up. Afterward, they sang silly ditties about the professors and football heroes. Each class had its own shout or song. The Class of 1904's bordered on the gruesome:

"Live man, sick man, dead man, stiff—
Catch 'em up, cut 'em up, what's the diff?
Humerus, tumerus, blood and gore,
U.B. Medics nineteen four." Courtesy University Archives.

At the turn of the century, medical and pharmacy students, who shared a building, enjoyed a friendly rivalry with the dental students, who were housed in a separate building. In 1899, the rivalry turned into a three-day brouhaha during which the "meds" and "pharms" destroyed a state-of-the-art laboratory in the dental building, illustrated in this yearbook drawing. Students even fell from the second and third stories of the buildings. Miraculously, no one was seriously injured. The faculty took a "boys will be boys" attitude and the brawling was repeated during the next few years. Eventually, the deans quarreled over who should pay damages to their respective buildings and put a stop to the disruptions. Courtesy University Archives.

After a day of serious dissection, medical students share a lighter moment in this photo from around 1900. Courtesy University Archives.

Fraternities cropped up at the University around the turn of the century. One of the first groups was the YMCA College Association, whose first action was to publish a handbook for students. Some fraternities emphasized scholarship or Bible study, but all included social activities. "Smokers," parties featuring food, drink, and smelly cigars, were popular, as illustrated in this drawing from the 1905 *Iris*. Each professional school was associated with at least one fraternity; other fraternities were open to all schools. Courtesy University Archives.

Alpha Omega Delta Fraternity, University—Buffalo, 1900.

This 1900 photo of Alpha Omega Delta fraternity was donated to the University Archives by the family of Dr. Charles L. Schang, Class of 1900, who is shown in the second row from the bottom, fifth from the right.

Three of the fraternities that maintained houses for members, shown in this picture from the 1904 *Iris,* were Omega Upsilon Phi, upper right; Alpha Omega Delta, lower right, and the I.C.I. Society, bottom left. As early as 1906, it was suggested that the University build a dormitory, but the first one was not built until the 1950s. The early Annual Circulars directed students to report to the registrar as soon as they arrived in the city, and the janitor would accompany them to "respectable" boarding houses to secure accommodations. Also pictured here are Buffalo General Hospital, upper left; the dissecting room, center left, and the Medical School, center right. Courtesy University Archives.

This 1900 photo, captioned "*Iris* Board at Work," is typical of the playful style of the early yearbooks. Courtesy University Archives.

At a time when many universities were operated by churches and limited their admissions accordingly, the University of Buffalo exhibited a surprising openness in its admission policy. Women and blacks were admitted at relatively early dates. The University's welcoming attitude was formalized in its 1920 fund-raising campaign slogan "For all Buffalo Boys and Girls—regardless of race, creed or class."

The first medical article published in the United States by a woman physician was printed in 1849 in the *Buffalo Medical Journal,* under the editorship of Dr. Austin Flint. It was written by Elizabeth Blackwell who, the same year, was the first woman to graduate from medical school in the nation. She graduated from Geneva Medical College, which had strong ties to Buffalo through its faculty. She was admitted by Dr. Charles Alfred Lee, dean of the faculty at Geneva, who at the same time was professor of pathology and materia medica at Buffalo. Dr. James Webster, who also taught at both schools, shook her hand and predicted, "You'll make a stir I can tell you." Her admission was supported by an editorial in the *Buffalo Medical Journal.* A stamp was issued in her honor in 1974. Photo courtesy Mildred Spencer Sanes.

Left: In 1876, Mary Blair Moody, age 40 and the mother of six, became the first woman to graduate from the University of Buffalo Medical School. Though some professors welcomed her, others hoped she would be the last. A few rough fellows greeted Mrs. Moody with catcalls or smoked excessively near her at recess, but most were willing to treat her fairly. Dr. Moody was an active physician and scientist, particularly concerned with preventive medicine. She was the first woman member of the Erie County Medical Society, a fellow of the American Association for the Advancement of Science, and a contributor to the *Buffalo Medical Journal.* She was a founder of the Women's Educational and Industrial Union in Buffalo in 1885, and the first supervisor of its program in Hygiene and Physical Education. *Courtesy Buffalo and Erie County Historical Society.*

Right: Joseph Robert Love, Class of 1880, was the first black graduate of the University. He played an important role in stimulating the political activity of the black population of Jamaica and in inspiring the racial consciousness of Marcus Garvey, the charismatic leader who organized the first important U.S. black nationalist movement. Born and raised in Nassau, Bahamas, he came to the United States as an adult, working with the Episcopal Church. He was ordained in Buffalo and began his medical training at the Medical School in preparation for missionary work in Haiti. At the alumni banquet held the year he graduated, the last regular toast was to "Our Colored Fellow-citizens." Dr. Love, in his eloquent response, predicted that soon blacks would enjoy equality. *Courtesy University Archives.*

Cornelius Dorsette, Class of 1882, third from the bottom, second from left, was the University's second black graduate and became a friend, colleague, and personal physician to the famous black educator and leader Booker T. Washington. Dr. Dorsette helped organize the National Medical Association of black doctors. Born into slavery in North Carolina in 1859, he came to the University after being rejected by the University Medical College of New York City because of his race. Courtesy University Archives.

In 1912 local residents were impressed to read in the newspaper that the Medical School had students from as far away as India, such as Grace Ilahi-Baksh, pictured here. Most students were residents of Western New York, other parts of the state, and nearby areas of Ontario and Pennsylvania, which were populated mostly by European immigrants and their descendents. Courtesy University Archives.

Women medical students gather in the library of the medical school in 1912. Three women graduated in the class of 1880, and women were represented in virtually all graduating classes thereafter. By 1889, there were enough women medical students to form their own study club. Before the 1970s, the percentage of women in the Medical School did not exceed 15 percent. The number of women steadily increased, and now about half of the Medical School's students are women. Courtesy University Archives.

Dr. Lillian Craig Randall, Class of 1891, founded Riverside Hospital, pictured above in the *Buffalo Medical Journal*, which later became Lafayette General Hospital. Besides administering the hospital, Dr. Randall maintained a first aid clinic in Black Rock and another on Swan Street. Courtesy History of Medicine Collection.

Harold Reist, Class of 1916, helped pay his way through medical school by selling aluminum pots and pans. A survey in 1913 found that 86 percent of students helped pay their own expenses, and that about 20 percent were self-supporting. They were mechanics, pattern makers, customs inspectors, railway mail clerks, gardeners, policemen, park employees, pilots, pursers, deckhands, waiters, motormen, conductors, insurance salesmen, chauffeurs, painters, decorators, night watchmen, bell boys and janitors. Courtesy University Archives.

Clubs in the early part of the century reflected the ethnic diversity of the student body. They included the Polish University Club, founded around 1907 and pictured here; the Marquette Club for Catholics, founded in 1914, and the Italian-American Club, founded in 1915. Courtesy University Archives.

Athletics at the University began with a football team in 1894. Dr. U. B. Stein, Class of 1896, was captain. This pioneer team not only lost all its games, but, the story goes, was beaten by every high school in the Buffalo area. Courtesy University Archives.

Those with a musical bent could join the University of Buffalo Banjo and Mandolin Club, which appeared in the 1900 *Iris.* Courtesy University Archives.

The University Band, which included medical students, is shown in 1920 in Lafayette Square. W. Yerby Jones, who was later professor of ophthalmology, is seated in the first row, third from left. Courtesy University Archives.

The melody for this *Alma Mater Song* was written by Walter S. Goodale, Class of 1903, better known for his work as administrator of the Buffalo City Hospital. The words have fallen out of favor, but the tune is still occasionally played. Courtesy University Archives.

This 1907 photo of medical students might have been taken across the street from the Medical School in the tavern of the German-American Brewery, which for years functioned as a student union and faculty lounge. Dr. Bernhardt Gottlieb, Class of 1921, remembers faculty and students as being the most regular and dependable customers of the establishment. With the purchase of a schooner of beer for ten cents, customers received pickled herring, pea soup, small franks, fair-sized hamburgers, pickles galore, and a mountain of rye bread on every table, not to mention celery, olives, red radishes, and sliced onions. Courtesy University Archives.

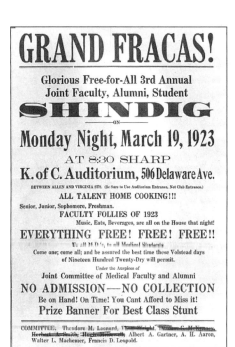

Raucous parties called shindigs were held for medical students, faculty, and alumni for several years beginning in 1921. They featured bawdy skits and plenty of booze, probably even during Prohibition. Women students objected to being barred, and shindigs gave way to coed dances in the 1940s. Courtesy University Archives.

The Alumni Club, which boasted about 800 members before the stock market crashed, aquired this clubhouse in 1921. The yellow brick mansion at 147 North Street was previously owned by General Edmund Hayes, for whom Hayes Hall is named. On the ground floor were a library, dining room, reading room, and reception area. The second floor had a large assembly hall and a card room and billiard room. Dormitory rooms took up the third floor. The garage at the rear of the house adjoining the tennis courts was converted into lockers, showers, and a dance floor. Dues were forty dollars a year. Courtesy University Archives.

The med students on the 1933 basketball team had their own prescription for success, according to a farcical article in the December issue of the *Medentian* magazine. They injected the ball with pilocarpine to shrink it as it left the shooter's hands, atropine to make the net look bigger, and caffeine to stimulate the ball. Courtesy University Archives.

The medical and dental student organizations in 1941 included, from left, top row, Nu Sigma Nu, Phi Lambda Kappa, and Phi Chi. Middle row: Alpha Omega Alpha, *Medentian* (the medical-dental yearbook), Med-Dent Student Council, and James A. Gibson Anatomical Society. Bottom row: Delta Sigma Delta, Xi Psi Phi, and Alpha Omega. Courtesy University Archives.

The Elizabeth Blackwell Society, named for the first woman medical graduate in the United States, was formed in 1946 by the twenty-three women medical students at the University. Part of the group is shown in this 1949 photo. Courtesy University Archives.

Students take a break between classes at the front entrance of the Medical School building on High Street in 1949. Courtesy University Archives.

At the same time the Medical School moved to the Main Street Campus, the University opened its first dormitories. Here students move into the new Schoellkopf residence hall in 1953. Courtesy University Archives.

Parking problems—and parking fees—are nothing new. In this 1958 photograph, it cost ten cents to park in the student lots on the Main-Bailey Campus. If you did not have change, you could not get out. Courtesy University Archives.

Army officer training was available to medical students in the 1950s, but the ROTC program was discontinued in the late 1960s when anti-military sentiment flared during the Vietnam conflict. Courtesy University Archives.

In the mid-1960s, new student groups were being formed, including the Benjamin Rush Society for students interested in psychiatry, and the Christian Medical Society, which still exist today. The Society on International Medicine was formed by William S. Resnick, Class of 1966, pictured above, who traveled to Africa during the summer after his junior year to fulfill his dream of working with Dr. Albert Schweitzer. Mr. Resnick died there in a swimming accident, three days after the famous doctor's death, and was buried beside him. Courtesy University Archives.

Students in 1989 kick up their heels during the annual spring Medical School Follies, which parodies the trials and tribulations of medical education. In the fall, a talent show spotlights the performing skills of students, faculty, administrators, and staff, and an art show is held in the spring. Courtesy University at Buffalo Publications Department.

Match Day, a time of tension and anticipation, erupted into a spontaneous celebration for these students in 1988 when they got the good news that they matched with the residencies of their choice. Courtesy University at Buffalo Publications Department.

Graduates sign the Book of Physicians and receive the distinctive hood at the commencement ceremony, pictured here in 1994. The academic regalia was designed by Dr. Robert L. Brown in 1971 for the Medical School's 125th anniversary. The gown is blue, a color of the University, and the hood and trim are hunter green, the traditional color of medicine. Courtesy University at Buffalo Publications Department.

The School's mace is carried during commencement by one of the marshals. Designed by Dr. Brown in 1968, it combines symbols of mythology, folklore, ancient traditions of medicine, and the University's history. Courtesy History of Medicine Collection.

In 1920, Walter P. Cooke, a prominent local lawyer and civic leader, assumed the chair of the University Council and quickly mobilized a city-wide campaign to raise funds in support of the Greater University of Buffalo movement. Modeled on the successful Liberty Loan Drives led by Mr. Cooke during World War I, the 1920 Endowment Fund Campaign raised $5 million in ten days from 24,000 subscribers. Courtesy University Archives.

Chapter 7

Between the World Wars

Expansion of the University marked the period between the two World Wars. The College of Arts and Sciences was in place. In order to develop the campus at Main and Bailey, in 1920 the University embarked on its first—and highly successful—Endowment Fund Campaign. Two years later, Samuel P. Capen, the first full-time chancellor, was appointed to guide the development of the Greater University.

Medical education was greatly influenced by the Flexner Report. By 1928, only 74 of the 155 medical schools investigated by Dr. Flexner remained. Scientific research changed the practice of medicine as well as the conduct of medical education, and medical schools became centers of research, increasingly supported by foundation grants and public funds. The trend toward specialization escalated. A study of graduates of the Medical School in Buffalo fifteen years after graduation showed that while 25 percent of the class of 1915 had become full-time specialists, 46 percent of the class of 1935 listed themselves as specialists.

Although the University increased its support of the Medical School, a series of poor evaluations by the accreditation teams of the American Medical Association demonstrated the precarious position of the School. During this difficult period, the volunteer faculty played a crucial role in maintaining high standards of clinical teaching; and, in spite of continuing financial hardship, the limited research space in the High Street building, and outdated facilities, the medical faculty made significant scientific contributions. These included the studies of Frank A. Hartman on the adrenal cortical hormones, which eventually led to the first successful treatment of Addison's Disease, and the work of Carl F. and Gerty Cori, who later received the Nobel Prize for their work on carbohydrate metabolism.

Posed here in front of the John J. Albright Mansion, the Women's Committee was one of the many volunteer groups responsible for the success of the 1920 Endowment Fund Campaign. The stone balustrade shown was removed when the Albright Mansion was razed in the mid-1930s and placed in front of the University's Lockwood Memorial Library (now the Health Sciences Library). Courtesy University Archives.

The success of the 1920 Endowment Fund Campaign led to the search for a full-time, salaried chief executive officer to guide the development of the Greater University. After a two-year search, Samuel P. Capen, the founding director of the American Council on Education, was selected. He is, at left, in academic robes speaking at the opening of the new Foster Hall, held in conjunction with his inauguration. Orin E. Foster, the donor of the building, is to the right of Capen, and Council Chairman Walter P. Cooke is smiling at far right. During his twenty-eight year tenure, Chancellor Capen transformed a loose collection of largely independent schools into a comprehensive university dedicated to the highest standards of academic excellence and service to the community. Courtesy University Archives.

This 1921 aerial photograph shows the County Almshouse property at Main and Bailey under development as the University campus. Main Street runs almost horizontally at the center of the photograph. At the left, Foster Hall—the first building to be erected by the University as a result of the 1920 endowment campaign—is under construction. To the right are the former almshouse buildings. The rectangle in front of the buildings was still a vegetable patch. There are few buildings in the Bailey-Winspear neighborhood. Courtesy University Archives.

Back Buffalo's Boys and Girls

UNIVERSITY OF BUFFALO $5,000,000 ENDOWMENT FUND CAMPAIGN

BUFFALO'S boys and girls are her richest treasure and her highest obligation! And what lies so close to the hearts and minds of Buffalo as their preparation for lives of idealism, achievement and service?

Back Buffalo's boys and girls! Back them with the most enduring of gifts—the fair chance for a college education. Today the University of Buffalo calls on every citizen to share this noble enterprise.

Great are the objectives of this campaign... new buildings... new equipment... but above all, ENDOWMENT—endowment which safeguards the accomplishments of today... fulfils the hopes and dreams of tomorrow!

The University of Buffalo Looks to You!

· · · · · · OCTOBER · 17 — 29 · 1929 · · · · · ·

From October 17 to October 29, 1929, the University conducted a second $5 million Endowment Fund Campaign. The appeal to local citizens was carried in newspaper ads, such as the one shown here, and posters displayed throughout the city. At the close of the campaign—on the same day the stock market crashed—the goal had been exceeded, but some of the pledges from 33,000 individuals were never received because of financial hardship. Courtesy University Archives.

A general practitioner, Albert Mott, Class of 1905, is shown in his office on Bailey and Kensington in 1931. In addition to his general practice, Dr. Mott delivered babies. He provided prenatal care at his office and, accompanied by his private obstetrical nurse, went to the patient's home for the delivery. Following a stroke in 1942, Dr. Mott gave up his obstetrical practice, although he continued his general practice for some time. Courtesy Ronald E. Batt, M.D.

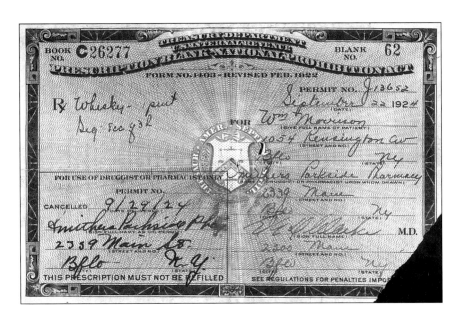

Since time immemorial, wine and spirits have been used for medicinal purposes. Self-medication with alcohol was not allowed during Prohibition and a prescription, such as this one written in 1924 for one pint of whiskey, was required. Courtesy Sisters Hospital Archives.

During the Great Depression, the Outpatient Department of the Buffalo General Hospital, founded in 1928, treated a record number of patients. It played a major role in the education of medical students, interns, and residents. Courtesy Buffalo General Hospital Archives.

The waiting room of the Outpatient Department of the Buffalo General Hospital, shown here, was always crowded during the Great Depression and patients were charged only what they could pay. One year, the average cost per visit was four and one-half cents. Courtesy Buffalo General Hospital Archives.

In the 1920s and 1930s, patients with tuberculosis were often confined to the Buffalo City Hospital for months. When ambulatory, they worked at a variety of tasks in hospital workshops. Patients who were convalescing at home were given lunch and streetcar fare to come to the workshop. The products were sold and the profit divided between the patient and the hospital. Here men refinish and reupholster furniture. Courtesy Erie County Medical Center.

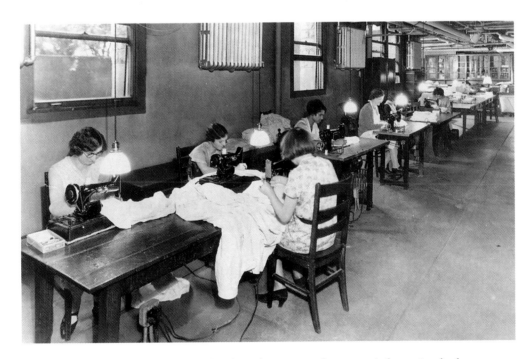

Patients confined to bed with tuberculosis were often occupied weaving baskets, knitting, carving, and building ship models. This photograph shows ambulatory women patients sewing at Buffalo City Hospital. Courtesy Erie County Medical Center.

Frank A. Hartman, professor and chairman of the Department of Physiology from 1918 to 1934, was one of the first to study the adrenal cortical hormones. He purified cortin and his work eventually led to the first effective treatment of Addison's Disease. Dr. Hartman received the Chancellor's Medal from the University and the Gold Medal of the American Medical Association. Courtesy Physiology Department.

Dr. Carl F. Cori and his wife, Dr. Gerty Cori, studied medicine at the German University at Prague. In 1922, they came to Buffalo to work on carbohydrate metabolism at the New York State Institute for the Study of Malignant Diseases, today the Roswell Park Cancer Institute. For their work they received the Nobel Prize in Physiology and Medicine in 1947. Courtesy History of Medicine Collection.

In 1929, Dr. Carl Cori helped recruit Kornel L. Terplan, pictured here in his brain laboratory at Children's Hospital. Dr. Terplan was a native of Transylvania and received his M.D. from the German University at Prague. He served as pathologist at both the Buffalo General Hospital and at Children's Hospital and was chairman of the Department of Pathology from 1930 to 1965. He is recognized for his work in childhood tuberculosis and brain pathology associated with chromosome anomalies of children. Courtesy Ronald E. Batt, M.D.

Dr. Terplan recruited Ernest Witebsky to his department in 1938. In the early 1940s, Dr. Witebsky, left, who was later named distinguished professor, together with Niels Klendshoj, right, isolated the B-antigen found in human blood that made blood transfusions safer. Dr. Witebsky continued his pioneering studies in autoimmune disease and its relation to thyroiditis, Addison's Disease, and myasthenia gravis. In 1967, Dr. Witebsky was appointed director of the newly created Center for Immunology and, upon his death in 1969, the center was named in his honor. Courtesy History of Medicine Collection.

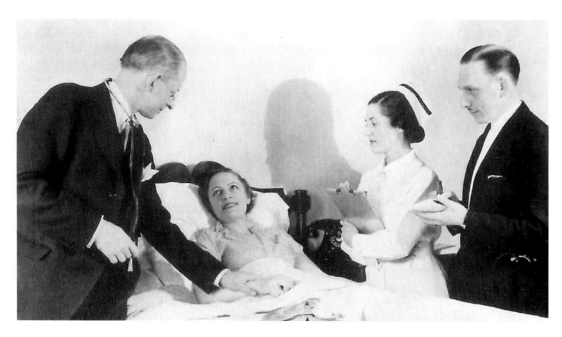

Throughout the history of the Medical School, the volunteer faculty have been indispensable to clinical teaching. In this photo from 1934, Clayton Greene and Harry LaForge, then a resident, conduct midnight rounds at Buffalo General Hospital. Dr. Greene recorded the first electrocardiogram in the area in 1914 and became the first clinical cardiologist in Buffalo. Later the cardiology and pulmonary research program under Drs. David Greene and Ivan Bunnell was developed. This long and careful preparation made the Buffalo General Hospital the logical site for the development of cardiac surgery under Drs. John R. Paine and George Schimert and, more recently, the upstate center for cardiac and pulmonary transplantation surgery. Courtesy Buffalo General Hospital Archives.

Nelson G. Russell, Class of 1895, leads rounds in 1936 at Buffalo General Hospital. Dr. Russell was one of the most influential clinicians in Buffalo for more than sixty years. He served on the faculty of the Medical School and as chief of medicine at Buffalo General Hospital. An expert in pulmonary tuberculosis, he conducted his own autopsies to learn more about the causes of disease. In 1945, he received the Chancellor's Medal for his work as a scientist, teacher, and mentor of two generations of physicians. Courtesy Buffalo General Hospital Archives.

Four leaders of the Buffalo medical community gather in the prescription department of a new National Drug Store with W. A. Harvey, vice president of the National Drug Corporation. From left are Mr. Harvey; Dr. Clayton W. Greene, associate professor of medicine, Dr. Nelson G. Russell, professor of medicine; Dr. Walter S. Goodale, professor of hygiene and public health and administrator of the Buffalo City Hospital, and Dr. Edward J. Meyer, clinical professor of surgery. Courtesy Buffalo General Hospital Archives.

The Main Street Campus circa 1940 housed the College of Arts and Sciences and the School of Pharmacy. Some of the buildings in the 1921 aerial photo (page 135) have been torn down or replaced. Hayes Hall and what are now Wende and Townsend are original county buildings that were remodeled. The campus plan was developed by the famous architect E. B. Green who also designed the original Lockwood Memorial Library, now the Health Sciences Library. Courtesy University Archives.

4th Annual Spring Clinical Day
ALUMNI ASSOCIATION
University of Buffalo, School of Medicine

SATURDAY, April 23, 1938, BUFFALO, N.Y.

HOTEL STATLER

"The Reason for Subtotal Gastrectomy for the Radical Cure of Gastric and Duodenal Ulcer."
A. A. BERG, M. D., Consulting Surgeon to Mt. Sinai Hospital, New York City

"Nephritis " WILLIAM BOYD, M.D.,
Professor of Pathology, University of Toronto, Toronto, Ont.

"Allergy in General Practice." ROBERT A. COOKE, M. D.,
Assistant Professor of Clinical Medicine, Cornell University Medical College, New York City

"The Diagnosis and Surgical Treatment of Hyperthyroidism."
DONALD GUTHRIE. M. D., Chief of Staff of Guthrie Clinic, Sayre, Pa.

"The Importance of the Valvular Lesion in Rheumatic Heart Disease."
SAMUEL A. LEVINE, M. D., Assistant Professor of Medicine, Harvard University Medical School, Boston, Mass.

"The Clinical Significance of Visual, Fundal and Visual Field Changes produced by Intracranial Lesions." WALTER I. LILLIE M.D.,
Professor of Ophthalmology, Temple University, Philadelphia, Pa.

"The Practical Management of the Pernicious Anemia Patient."
WILLIAM P. MURPHY, M.D., Associate in Medicine, Harvard Medical School, Boston, Mass.

The Profession is cordially invited to attend on the same fee basis as regular Alumni members -- namely, current year's dues of three dollars.

ANNUAL DINNER at 7:00 P.M. - - - Tickets Two Dollars.
Hon. SAMUEL B. PETTENGILL,
Member U.S. House of Representatives from Indiana.
"Looking for the Fire Escape."

The first Spring Clinical Day was sponsored by the Alumni Association in 1935. For the annual event, the Medical Alumni Association invites distinguished speakers to deliver the Stockton Kimball Lecture, named for Dr. Kimball who served as dean of the Medical School from 1946 to 1958. Five-year class reunions are held in conjunction with the event. Courtesy University Archives.

Chapter 8

World War II, Optimism and Expansion

World War II brought dramatic changes to medical practice and education. Federal funding increased substantially following the war and, as a result, medical schools emphasized research, both in the basic sciences and in clinical medicine. Full-time faculty and unpaid volunteers replaced part-time faculty. Student enrollment increased with the introduction of the GI Bill of Rights, leading to the establishment of new medical schools throughout the country. Many medical schools developed into academic health centers, which included one or more health profession schools and affiliation with teaching hospitals.

In Buffalo, the war had taken its toll on the Medical School. Many volunteer and full-time faculty served in the armed forces. Those who stayed behind placed their energies on patient care and teaching while research suffered. In 1945, the Accreditation Team of the American Medical Association recommended that the Medical School in Buffalo be placed on probation. Once again, the School was forced to change.

A new medical school complex was constructed on Main and Bailey where all other schools and departments except Law were located. The completion of Sherman Hall in 1958 greatly expanded the research facilities, and the clinical departments based in the affiliated hospitals brought further distinction to the School. In order to support continuing medical education, a group of physicians in the Medical School organized the Annual Participating Fund for Medical Education.

Facing page: The freshman class wondered if the war would keep them from their studies, as depicted in this cartoon from the 1941 yearbook. Shortly after the United States declared war in 1941, medical students were inducted into the armed services. By the following summer, the curriculum had been reorganized into a three-year program with classes continuing throughout the year. Specialized training units were formed within the Medical School. Every morning the students would line up in uniform in front of the High Street building and march to a nearby field for drill exercises. Courtesy University Archives.

Dr. Fred R. Griffith, professor of physiology, lectures to a class of medical school students, most in uniform, in 1941. Courtesy University Archives.

During the 1950s it became increasingly evident that the University of Buffalo could not by itself develop into a major private University. Negotiations with the State University of New York led to a merger agreement that became effective in September 1962. After the merger, the University received unprecedented funding to build the Amherst (North) Campus, update the Main Street (South) Campus, increase enrollment and hire full-time faculty.

Below: In 1940, Buffalo General Hospital was chosen as one of sixty-five hospitals throughout the country to form an army hospital. The unit, which became known as the Twenty-third U.S. Army General Hospital, is shown in 1943 at Fort Meade, Maryland. Courtesy Buffalo General Hospital Archives.

The Twenty-third General Hospital opened a 1,000-bed general hospital, first in Naples, Italy, and later in Vittel, France, shown here, and treated more than 53,000 war casualties. Courtesy Buffalo General Hospital Archives.

Soldiers return to Buffalo victorious. Encouraged by their experiences in World War II and funded by the GI Bill of Rights, many returning physicians entered residency programs in the specialties. Courtesy History of Medicine Collection.

Stockton Kimball served as the eighteenth dean of the Medical School from 1946 to 1958. Under his leadership the School became nationally prominent and developed its education and research activities. Born in Buffalo in 1902, Dr. Kimball received his undergraduate degree from Harvard and his M.D. from Buffalo. He studied in England and Germany before returning to Buffalo to practice medicine. As dean, he guided the development of the School following the Second World War, directed the move from High Street to the Main Street Campus, and helped lay the groundwork for the merger into the State University system. Today, distinguished research by University faculty is recognized by the Stockton Kimball Award named for him. Courtesy University Archives.

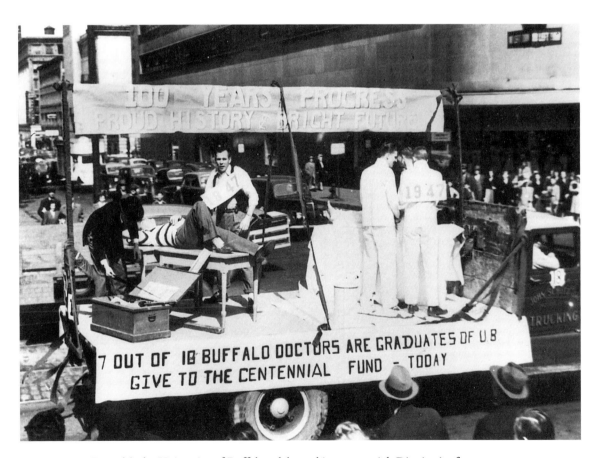

In 1946, the University of Buffalo celebrated its centennial. Dignitaries from many universities across the country attended academic exercises presided over by Chancellor Capen. Dr. Clayton Greene organized the activities of the Medical School and medical students built a float for the occasion. Courtesy University Archives.

The elegant building on High Street was no longer able to meet the needs of the expanding Medical School. The University attempted to sell the building, but was unsuccessful. The emphasis on historic preservation had not yet occurred, and in 1954 the structure was demolished. Courtesy History of Medicine Collection.

In 1956, the Medical School received the largest bequest in its history up to that time. Ralph Hochstetter, president of Cliff Petroleum Company, gave half of his investments totaling $8 million to support fellowships in medical research. Named in honor of Henry C. Buswell, professor of medicine at Niagara University, pictured here, and his wife, Bertha Hochstetter Buswell, the endowment significantly strengthened basic research at the School. Courtesy History of Medicine Collection.

The bequest of DeWitt H. Sherman for a medical research building further strengthened the research efforts of the School. Dr. Sherman, professor of pediatrics, died in 1940 and the funds became available upon the death of his wife in 1957. The Sherman Hall addition to Capen Hall, dedicated in 1958, provided needed laboratory space for the expansion of the Department of Physiology and the development of the Biophysics Department. This photo shows Fred Snell, chairman, in the machine shop of the Biophysics Department. Courtesy University Archives.

The new Medical and Dental School building, Capen Hall (now Farber Hall) on Bailey Avenue opened for classes in September 1953. It provided greatly increased space and modern equipment for instruction in the basic sciences. Courtesy University Archives.

153

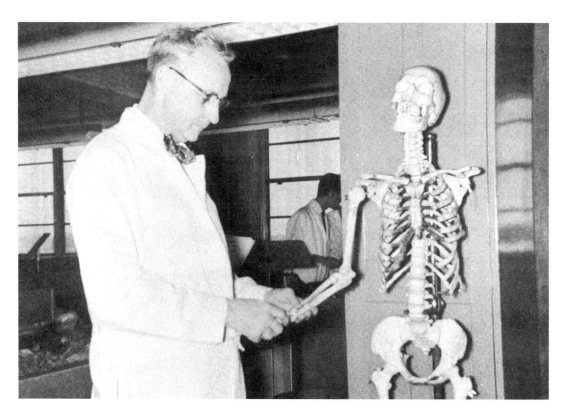

Oliver P. Jones, distinguished professor, was widely recognized for his studies in morphological hematology and for his work in pernicious anemias, placental transfer of antianemic substances, and in the classification of mechanisms of abnormalities of erythropoiesis, which have become classics in the field. He is shown here in the gross anatomy laboratory in the Medical School in 1956. In addition to heading the Department of Anatomy from 1943 to 1971, he also served as assistant dean in charge of admissions from 1946 to 1955, and he introduced electron microscopy to the Medical School. After his retirement, he devoted his energies to the study of the early history of the Medical School. Courtesy History of Medicine Collection.

David K. Miller was the first full-time professor of a clinical department at the Medical School. A graduate of Harvard Medical School, he worked for six years at the Rockefeller Institute. In September of 1939 he was appointed director of laboratories at Buffalo City Hospital and, two years later, was promoted to professor of medicine. After the war, federal funding helped support full-time clinical faculty and the clinical departments expanded greatly. Among the first full-time clinical faculty were John D. Stewart, professor of surgery, and Mitchell I. Rubin, professor of pediatrics. Courtesy University Archives.

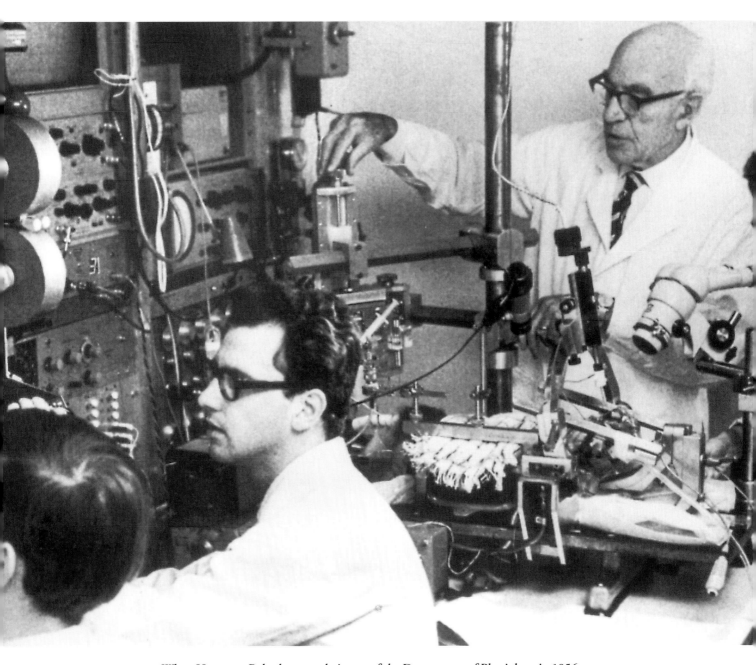

When Hermann Rahn became chairman of the Department of Physiology in 1956, he was given the opportunity to build a new staff as well as design Sherman Hall. He attracted an outstanding faculty, including John C. Eccles, Nobel Laureate, at right, who joined the group in 1968. Dr. Rahn, a member of the National Academy of Sciences, was named distinguished professor in 1972. Courtesy University Archives.

Samuel Sanes, Class of 1930, was a faculty member for more than thirty years, teaching pathology and legal medicine. In the 1950s, Dr. Sanes was coordinator of *Modern Medicine*, one of the first medical shows on television. He was also a moderator of the University's *Summer Medical Roundtable*, a talk show first on radio, then television. He was dedicated to educating the public, and, when he contracted cancer in 1973, he wrote a series of articles for the *Buffalo Physician* on what he learned being a patient. Here the much-loved teacher gives his final lecture before his death in 1978. Courtesy Mildred Spencer Sanes.

In the late 1950s and early 1960s, three important contributions to medicine provided international recognition to Buffalo physicians. The first successful, internal cardiac pacemaker was developed by a team that included two members of the Department of Surgery, Drs. William Chardack and Andrew Gage, and Mr. Wilson Greatbatch, an engineer. Here the pacemaker is compared in size to a pack of matches. Dr. Jack Lippes, professor of gynecology-obstetrics, began work on the design and commercial availability of the intrauterine contraceptive device that became known as the Lippes Loop, and Dr. Robert Guthrie, professor of pediatrics, described the methodology to screen infants for phenylketonuria (PKU). Courtesy Andrew Gage, M.D.

In the 1950s, the Chronic Disease Research Institute, located on the grounds of the old United States Marine Hospital at 2211 Main Street next to Sisters Hospital, was devoted to the study of chronic diseases with special reference to disorders of the heart, blood vessels, lungs and kidneys. Later, the building was occupied by the Department of Social and Preventive Medicine. Courtesy University Archives.

The Chronic Disease Research Institute was the site of many interdisciplinary research activities. Pictured above are Walter F. Stafford, neurologist in the polio-respirator center; Walter T. Zimdahl, director of the institute, and Arthur E. MacNeill, chief of laboratories. Courtesy University Archives.

Trained at Johns Hopkins Medical School by the famous medical illustrator Max Brodel, Melford D. Diedrick became the first medical illustrator at the University. His clear drawings enhanced many scientific articles and books written by the faculty. Courtesy Melford D. Diedrick.

On November 28, 1960, the University Council, shown here with Chairman Seymour H. Knox presiding, took the first step toward the merger of the University with the expanding State University of New York. At this meeting, the council authorized a committee to pursue discussions. After months of complex negotiations, an agreement was reached, and on September 1, 1962, the private university became the State University of New York at Buffalo, still affectionately known as UB. Courtesy University Archives.

This is a view of the campus shortly after the merger. Courtesy University Archives.

Sean Perini, Class of 1994, explains his work to Dr. Chris Cohan, associate professor of anatomy and cell biology, at the 1991 Medical Student Research Forum. Students have competed with distinction at national forums and for prestigious fellowships such as the Howard Hughes Institute Fellowship. The Medical School provides stipends for summer research. A seven-year integrated M.D./Ph.D. program has been established to develop a cadre of up to five clinical scientists entering each year. Courtesy University at Buffalo Publications Department.

Chapter 9

From the Merger to the Present

The anticipation and expectation that surrounded the 1962 merger of the private University of Buffalo with the State University system proved unsettling for the Medical School: Periods of great expectation were too often followed by periods of severe disillusionment as exciting plans were scaled back or never realized. It was not until 1973 that the Medical School's course was steadied when Dr. F. Carter Pannill was appointed vice president for Health Sciences. Under his leadership, John Naughton was recruited as dean of the Medical School and assumed the post in March 1975.

Under Dr. Naughton's stewardship, the Medical School grew and expanded in many directions. While maintaining its historical commitment to clinical and research excellence and strong education of medical students and residents, the Medical School developed a broader biomedical research and training program. To reflect this expanded role, in 1987 the School changed its name to the School of Medicine and Biomedical Sciences. Today the Medical School is considered a leader among the nation's comprehensive medical schools.

Medical Student Education

The Medical School devotes much of its fund-raising efforts toward scholarship support for meritorious and deserving students. A generous endowment established by Harold S. and Thelma Sanes provides one full scholarship for one student in each class. Recent recipients include from left, Joy Nwachukwu, Class of 1999; Angela Camasto, Class of 1997, and Dr. Barbara Kearney Stefanick, Class of 1994, gathered in front of the Health Sciences Library. Other sources of scholarship support include Dr. Clara March, Dr. Mark Welch, Dr. Lloyd H. Leve, and the Ford Foundation. Photo by James A. Ulrich, University Academic Services/Computing and Information Technology.

Medical education now includes more than lectures and labs. New strategies include the use of standardized or surrogate patients—normal subjects who simulate clinical conditions and symptoms—as well as computer assisted education. A regional information network (HUBNET) electronically links the University, the Medical School, and its teaching hospitals. Long-distance learning and video teleconferencing capacities provide students, residents, physicians, and other health professionals with on-line access to a common patient index, exchange of medical reports and scans, and improved communication, as well as the extensive bibliographic and medical data bases maintained through the Health Sciences Library. More than 7,000 subscribers were using the system in January 1995. Photo by James A. Ulrich, University Academic Services.

The Museum of Neuroanatomy, the only museum of its kind in the United States, was created in 1994 by Dr. Harold Brody, Class of 1961, Distinguished Teaching Professor of Anatomy and Cell Biology. Located in the Cary-Farber-Sherman Building, the museum includes eighty individually lighted brain specimens exhibited in ten display cases, along with color photos, x-rays, and CT, MRI, and PET scans of the human brain. In addition to serving medical and health related students, the museum has become a major resource for the education of secondary school students in their science courses from public and private schools throughout Buffalo. Courtesy University at Buffalo Publications Department.

Graduate Medical Education

The Medical School worked with its affiliated hospitals to form the Graduate Medical Dental Education Consortium of Buffalo in 1985 to govern residency and fellowship training. The consortium led the reform of graduate medical education with its emphasis on training of primary care practitioners. In addition to the more traditional hospital settings, residents and students can train in rural locations, community health facilities, or physicians' offices.

The Primary Care Resource Center provides the necessary coordination among the disciplines of Family Medicine, General Internal Medicine, General Pediatrics, and Gynecology-Obstetrics to ensure development of primary care faculty, health related research programs, and recruitment and retention of primary care trainees. Depicted is a Primary Care Academic Practice Site in which residents and students are educated in a manner similar to an office setting. Courtesy University at Buffalo Publications Department.

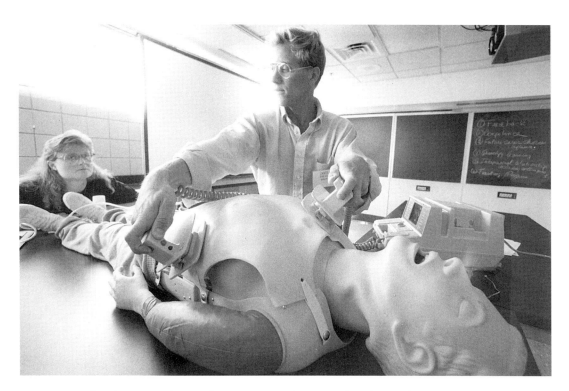

Before beginning his residency training, a new resident learns the principles and practice of advanced life support. This training is part of a week-long comprehensive orientation to residency introduced by the consortium. Courtesy University at Buffalo Publications Department.

The Office of Rural Health was established in the Medical School in 1987. It has facilitated development of a regional telecommunications network. The network comprises seven rural sites that are connected by fiber optic cable to urban hospitals affiliated with the Medical School. In minutes, medical specialists in tertiary hospitals can "examine" rural patients, such as this one in Cuba, New York, via video screen and consult with the rural physician on diagnosis and treatment. These capacities facilitate professional integration of physicians practicing in remote rural areas with the Buffalo urban center. Courtesy University at Buffalo Publications Department.

Research Programs

Entrance into the SUNY system provided the opportunity for the Medical School to develop a major biomedical research program. The Medical School's annual research support, combined with the research conducted under the auspices of the Roswell Park Cancer Institute, now exceeds $60 million, placing Buffalo among the top twenty medical research communities in the country.

Above: Facilities for the teaching laboratories in the basic sciences have been consolidated in the Cary-Farber-Sherman Hall complex on the South Campus. The addition shown here was built in 1987. Courtesy University at Buffalo Publications Department.

Facing page: Among the School's many organized research programs are: the Center for Advanced Molecular Biology and Immunology (CAMBI), the Positron Emission Tomography Center (PET), the Toxicology Research Center, the Women's Health Initiative, the Markey Foundation-sponsored Center for Molecular Parasitology, and the Perinatology-Neonatology Research Center. In this picture underwater breathing apparatus is being tested at the Center for Research and Education in Special Environments in its Hermann Rahn Laboratory for Environmental Physiology. Other areas such as high and low-atmospheric pressures, high-gravitational loads, and temperature extremes are also being studied. Courtesy University at Buffalo Publications Department.

A new research building, center, equipped with sixty laboratories, was dedicated in the sesquicentennial year. This modular 110,000-square-foot laboratory building houses Medical School and extramural research enterprises. Photo by James A. Ulrich, University Academic Services.

In 1985, the History of Medicine Collection was named for Robert L. Brown, Class of 1944, in recognition of his support of the Health Sciences Library. As associate dean, Dr. Brown improved the library's funding and initiated a program to rebind and conserve the long-neglected rare book collection. In 1974, he became Medical School archivist and began a systematic search for the historical records of the School. The History of Medicine Collection contains more than 12,000 monographs together with a pre-1940 journal collection of 30,000 volumes. In addition to the major donations of the nineteenth and early twentieth centuries, more recent rare book donations include the private collections of Dr. L. Maxwell Lockie, Class of 1929; Dr. Walter Stafford, Class of 1944; Dr. Joseph I. Schultz, Class of 1957, and Dr. Louis Bakay, professor emeritus of neurosurgery. Courtesy History of Medicine Collection.

In 1962 the Medical-Dental Library was renamed the Health Sciences Library and incorporated into the University Libraries. Today the Health Sciences Library is one of the major biomedical libraries in the country with a collection of more than 300,000 volumes, 2,300 serials, and more than 2,000 audiovisual titles. It supports the schools of Medicine, Dentistry, Nursing, Pharmacy, and Health Related Professions and serves as the health information resource center for Western New York. In 1985, the library moved into the former Lockwood Library, which had been renovated. This photograph shows the elegant Main Reading Room, which was adapted from the great hall at Hatfield House outside London built in the first decade of the seventeenth century for Sir Robert and Sir William Cecil. Courtesy History of Medicine Collection.

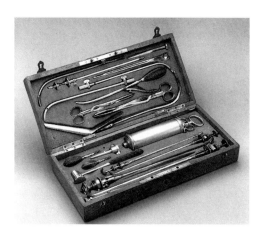

The Medical Historical Instrument Collection was established in 1985 by Mrs. Annette Cravens in memory of her father, Edgar R. McGuire, who served as chair of the Department of Surgery from 1914 to 1931. The collection includes instruments chosen for their illustration of past medical and dental practices. The collection has been expanded through other notable donations, which include a Powell and Lealand No.1 Stand Microscope from 1884 donated by Dr. William H. Merrilees; a naval surgical kit from 1840 donated by Dr. Theodore C. Jewett Jr., Class of 1945, and x-ray tubes from the early 1900s donated by Dr. Richard C. Batt, Class of 1936. Illustrated is a handsome set of lithotomy and lithotrity instruments manufactured by Charriere circa 1840. Courtesy History of Medicine Collection.

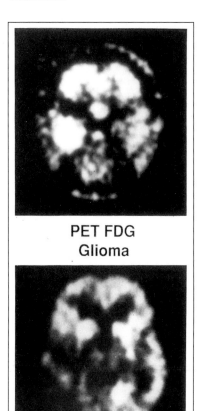

PET FDG
Glioma

PET FDG
Necrosis

A Positron Emission Tomography (PET) Center was established in 1993. The cyclotron for producing the short-lived radioactive isotopes is located in Parker Hall on the South Campus. One PET scanner is based at the VA Medical Center and one at the Millard Fillmore Hospital at Gates Circle. The PET Center was financed by the VA Medical Center, the University, and a $1 million gift from Buffalo's James H. Cummings Foundation. The two images here show PET scans of brains made with FDG, a radioactive form of glucose. In the top picture, the large white circle on the left of the brain shows a glioma or tumor. In the bottom picture, the black area at the lower left shows necrosis, where tumor tissue has been successfully destroyed by radiation treatment. Other imaging techniques cannot distinguish between live and dead tissue. Courtesy Department of Nuclear Medicine.

172

Herbert Hauptman, research professor of biophysics, won the Nobel Prize in Chemistry in 1985. A renowned mathematician, he is president of the Hauptman-Woodward Medical Research Institute Inc., formerly the Medical Foundation of Buffalo. Dr. Hauptman and his collaborator, Dr. Jerome Karle, devised what is now the standard method to determine the three-dimensional structures of complex molecules. This has enabled researchers to identify and manipulate molecules and to develop countless new drugs, including vitamins, antibiotics, hypertension medications, artificial steroids, and hormones. Courtesy University at Buffalo Publications Department.

Clinical Enterprise

When the University entered the SUNY system, most of the Medical School faculty members were volunteers. Today, there are about 500 full-time academic clinical faculty, with a dedicated and skilled volunteer staff of 1,500 as well.

The Medical School has maintained its tradition of using a distributive model for clinical education, combining a strong foundation in the sciences with diverse clinical experiences.

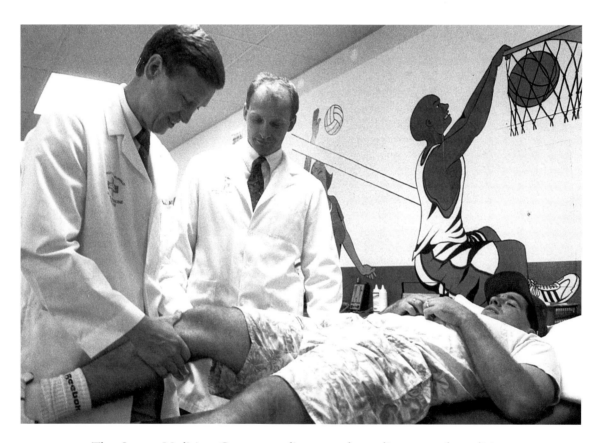

The Sports Medicine Center coordinates orthopaedics, general medicine, biomechanical research and physical therapy activities for teaching, research, and care of acute and chronic sports injuries. Photo by James A. Ulrich, University Academic Services.

The University Physicians' Office, located in the Medical School, provides ambulatory care teaching opportunities to medical and health science students. Continuity of patient care is emphasized. Photo by James A. Ulrich, University Academic Services.

Ancillary Organizations

The School's work is facilitated through many support groups, including the Medical Alumni Association, the James Platt White Society, and the Parents Council.

The Medical Alumni support many medical student and resident activities, such as Spring Clinical Day, a scientific conference held every spring. Pictured here, Dr. James Todd, executive vice president of the American Medical Association, addressed faculty and students on "Doctor Watchers" in 1993. Courtesy University at Buffalo Publications Department.

The Medical Alumni Association established a Distinguished Medical Alumnus Award in 1989. The first recipient was Dr. George W. Thorn, Class of 1929, who grew up in Buffalo. He collaborated with Dr. Frank A. Hartman, chairman of physiology, on work that led to the first successful treatment of Addison's Disease. Dr. Thorn and Dr. Hartman received the Gold Medal of the American Medical Association for the work. In 1942, Dr. Thorn became Hersey Professor of Theory and Practice of Physic at the Harvard Medical School, and in 1969 he was appointed Samuel A. Levine Professor of Medicine at Harvard. He was one of the original four members of the Advisory Board of the Howard Hughes Medical Institute and, in 1984, was appointed chairman of the Board of Trustees. Throughout his distinguished career, Dr. Thorn's research has been concentrated in endocrinology and metabolism. Courtesy Medical Alumni Association.

Professor William R. Greiner, president of the University at Buffalo, joined the law faculty in 1967 and subsequently held several administrative positions in the School of Law. In the early 1980s he became active in University-wide administration and was named the University's first provost in 1984. He was appointed president in 1991. He holds a B.A. in economics from Wesleyan University, and a master's degree in economics and master's and doctoral degrees in law, all from Yale University. Under his leadership, the University has reemphasized its commitment to public service. Courtesy University at Buffalo Publications Department.

Dr. John Naughton became dean of the Medical School in 1975, with a well-established career in academic medicine that included training and academic leadership roles at the universities of Oklahoma and Illinois and at George Washington University. He is an established national leader in exercise physiology, exercise testing, and rehabilitation of myocardial infarction patients. He led the School of Medicine and Biomedical Sciences through a period of considerable growth and development and his advice and counsel have been sought by national academic medicine leaders and councils. Courtesy University at Buffalo Publications Department.

The new medical research building, photographed by James A. Ulrich, University Academic Services/Computing and Information Technology.

The Future

Observation of the University's sesquicentennial in 1996 provides that rare opportunity to review and appreciate the trials, tribulations and achievements of the past and present and the prospects of a great future.

For all medical schools, the next fifty years will present new and exciting challenges that will span the continued need to develop new basic knowledge designed to benefit patients as individuals and society as a whole. However, with an increasing life span and many citizens deprived of even minimal medical and health services, medical education must concentrate more on issues of preventive and community medicine, evolution of therapeutic effectiveness, and comprehensive, continuous medical and health care that is system, not disease, oriented.

The University Medical School will always be committed to the education of its students in the fundamentals of medicine. Given the accomplishments of the past 150 years, the school is poised to continue this tradition and to respond to the unmet needs of biomedical sciences and the unmet health care needs of its citizens.

John Naughton, M.D.
Vice President for Clinical Affairs
Dean of the School of Medicine and Biomedical Sciences

The Departments

Many of the Medical School's departments are direct offshoots of earlier departments, created as the practice of medicine became more specialized. New knowledge, new technology, and changing roles have produced new departments such as Radiology and Biophysical Sciences. Charts by Ronald E. Batt, M.D.

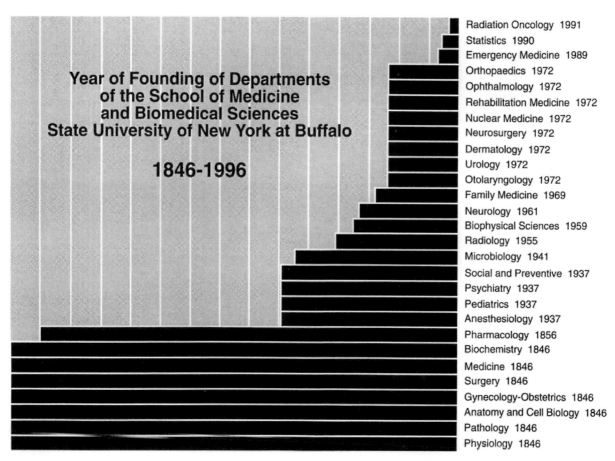

Year of Founding of Departments of the School of Medicine and Biomedical Sciences State University of New York at Buffalo

1846-1996

Radiation Oncology 1991
Statistics 1990
Emergency Medicine 1989
Orthopaedics 1972
Ophthalmology 1972
Rehabilitation Medicine 1972
Nuclear Medicine 1972
Neurosurgery 1972
Dermatology 1972
Urology 1972
Otolaryngology 1972
Family Medicine 1969
Neurology 1961
Biophysical Sciences 1959
Radiology 1955
Microbiology 1941
Social and Preventive 1937
Psychiatry 1937
Pediatrics 1937
Anesthesiology 1937
Pharmacology 1856
Biochemistry 1846
Medicine 1846
Surgery 1846
Gynecology-Obstetrics 1846
Anatomy and Cell Biology 1846
Pathology 1846
Physiology 1846

1846 1856 1866 1876 1886 1896 1906 1916 1926 1936 1946 1956 1966 1976 1986 1996

Year of Founding

Source: Annual Bulletins, School of Medicine, 1846–1996.

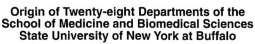

**Origin of Twenty-eight Departments of the
School of Medicine and Biomedical Sciences
State University of New York at Buffalo**

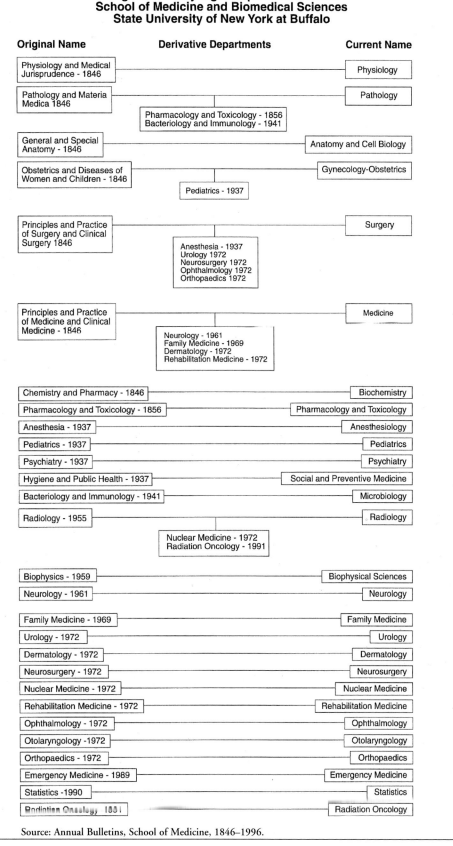

Original Name	Derivative Departments	Current Name
Physiology and Medical Jurisprudence - 1846		Physiology
Pathology and Materia Medica 1846		Pathology
	Pharmacology and Toxicology - 1856 Bacteriology and Immunology - 1941	
General and Special Anatomy - 1846		Anatomy and Cell Biology
Obstetrics and Diseases of Women and Children - 1846		Gynecology-Obstetrics
	Pediatrics - 1937	
Principles and Practice of Surgery and Clinical Surgery 1846		Surgery
	Anesthesia - 1937 Urology 1972 Neurosurgery 1972 Ophthalmology 1972 Orthopaedics 1972	
Principles and Practice of Medicine and Clinical Medicine - 1846		Medicine
	Neurology - 1961 Family Medicine - 1969 Dermatology - 1972 Rehabilitation Medicine - 1972	
Chemistry and Pharmacy - 1846		Biochemistry
Pharmacology and Toxicology - 1856		Pharmacology and Toxicology
Anesthesia - 1937		Anesthesiology
Pediatrics - 1937		Pediatrics
Psychiatry - 1937		Psychiatry
Hygiene and Public Health - 1937		Social and Preventive Medicine
Bacteriology and Immunology - 1941		Microbiology
Radiology - 1955		Radiology
	Nuclear Medicine - 1972 Radiation Oncology - 1991	
Biophysics - 1959		Biophysical Sciences
Neurology - 1961		Neurology
Family Medicine - 1969		Family Medicine
Urology - 1972		Urology
Dermatology - 1972		Dermatology
Neurosurgery - 1972		Neurosurgery
Nuclear Medicine - 1972		Nuclear Medicine
Rehabilitation Medicine - 1972		Rehabilitation Medicine
Ophthalmology - 1972		Ophthalmology
Otolaryngology -1972		Otolaryngology
Orthopaedics - 1972		Orthopaedics
Emergency Medicine - 1989		Emergency Medicine
Statistics -1990		Statistics
Radiation Oncology 1991		Radiation Oncology

Source: Annual Bulletins, School of Medicine, 1846–1996.

Time Line

1801   Dr. Cyrenius Chapin, Buffalo's first physician, settles in the region.

1813   British burn Buffalo, despite the negotiations of Dr. Chapin, a colonel during the War of 1812. Buffalonians soon rebuilt their village, starting, appropriately, with the Phoenix Tavern.

1843   Dr. Austin Flint's landmark study points to the source of the typhoid epidemic in the village of Boston, south of Buffalo.

1845   First issue of the *Buffalo Medical Journal* is published. The Buffalo Medical Association is formed to provide a free interchange of medical opinions.

1800–1819

1820–1839

1821   Erie County separates from Niagara County and the Medical Society of the County of Erie is founded. Early concerns were vital statistics and vaccination.

1825   The western terminus of the Erie Canal, more than seven years in the making, finally opened in Buffalo.

1832   Buffalo is incorporated as a city. Ebenezer Johnson, a physician, was the first mayor.

1832   Cholera epidemic sweeps across Western New York and Buffalo.

1836   University of Western New York is chartered, but closed after a few months.

1837   Dr. Josiah Trowbridge is the second physician to be elected mayor of Buffalo.

1840–1859

1846   The University of Buffalo is founded with the establishment of the Medical Department. Medical classes were first held in a converted church. The first class of Buffalo doctors was graduated in 1847. Dr. Frank Hastings Hamilton, professor of principles and practice of surgery and clinical surgery, is the dean.

1847   Dr. Hamilton is the first physician in Buffalo to use ether—for a patient with a dislocated shoulder. Manipulating the arm usually worked, but this big stevedore was so muscular even ropes and pulleys could not do the trick. The ether relaxed the muscles and the shoulder popped into place. When the patient awoke, he announced it was "the best grog" he ever had.

     Dr. Alden S. Sprague, vice president of the Buffalo Medical Association, performs the first major operation under anesthesia (amputation at the thigh) in Buffalo. The era of painless surgery began the year before when doctors in Boston gave a successful public demonstration of the use of ether in removing a jaw tumor.

1848   Millard Fillmore, chancellor of the University, is elected vice president of the United States.

     The Sisters of Charity open the first teaching hospital in Buffalo.

1849   The University constructs a medical school building at Main and Virginia Streets.

     Dr. Austin Flint, professor of principles and practice of medicine and clinical medicine, is named dean of the Medical School.

1850   James Platt White shows a live birth to his medical students, the first time demonstrative midwifery was used in the United States.

     Dr. Charles Brodhead Coventry, professor of physiology and medical jurisprudence, takes over as dean.

     Buffalo has become the thirteenth largest city in the United States, substantially larger than Detroit, Cleveland, or Chicago.

1852   James Platt White, professor of obstetrics and diseases of women and children, begins his first term as dean of the Medical School.

1854   Thomas F. Rochester, professor of principles and practice of medicine and clinical medicine, becomes dean.

1857   The annual report of the Health Department indicates that cholera infantum, typhoid, dysentery, smallpox, and diphtheria (known then as croup) were diseases of major importance. Rabies cases were frequently reported.

1858   Dr. Timothy T. Lockwood, an obstetrician and gynecologist, is the third doctor to be elected mayor of Buffalo.

     Buffalo General Hospital is dedicated.

1860   Dr. Sandford Eastman, professor of anatomy, is named dean of the Medical School and serves for six years.

1861   President Abraham Lincoln visits Buffalo on February 16, en route to his inauguration. He was welcomed at the Exchange Street train station by former president Millard Fillmore.

University hockey team, 1898. Courtesy University Archives.

1860–1879

1865   President Lincoln is shot April 14 and dies the next morning. His funeral cortege moved through Buffalo on its way from Washington, D.C.

1866   Dr. George Hadley, professor of chemistry and pharmacy, becomes dean.

High Street was paved and sewers were installed eight years after the founding of the Buffalo General Hospital.

1867-68   The Medical School has nine working teachers, and proudly notes that none is connected with any other institution.

Incoming students are advised that "Good board, with room, fuel and lights, can be found for $4.50 to $6 per week."

1869   Dr. Julius F. Miner, professor of special surgery, is named dean.

1872   Millard Fillmore Hospital is founded as the Buffalo Homeopathic Hospital.

1874   Dr. Milton G. Potter, professor of anatomy, is named dean.

1875   Dr. Thomas F. Rochester, professor of principles and practice of medicine and clinical medicine, is named acting dean; then appointed dean serving until 1878.

1876   Mary Blair Moody is the first woman to graduate from the Medical School.

Commencement program, 1876. Courtesy University Archives.

1878   The Medical School dispensed with the title and office of dean, and the president of the faculty took over those duties. Dr. James Platt White, professor of obstetrics and diseases of women and children, was named president of the faculty and served until his death September 28, 1881.

1880–1899

1880   Joseph Robert Love is the first black graduate of the Medical School.

1882   Dr. Charles Cary, professor of anatomy, is named dean.

1883   Thomas F. Rochester, vice chancellor of the University and professor of principles and practice of medicine and clinical medicine, becomes dean for the third time. He serves until his death May 24, 1887.

Niagara University starts a new medical school in Buffalo.

1884   Former Buffalo Mayor Grover Cleveland is elected president of the United States for the first time.

1886   The Pharmacy Department becomes the University's second division.

1887   Dr. Matthew D. Mann, professor of obstetrics and gynecology, is named acting dean, then dean, and serves for twenty-five years.

A Department of Veterinary Medicine was approved for the University but because of financial difficulties was never created.

1890   The Medical Practice Act created a State Medical Examining Board for New York.

1891   The Law Department, originally affiliated with Niagara University, is added.

1892   The Dental Department is added.

Buffalo's Grover Cleveland is elected president of the United States for the second time.

Several medical societies coalesce into the Buffalo Academy of Medicine.

Children's Hospital of Buffalo is founded.

1893   The Medical School moves into a new building on High Street.

1898   The Niagara University Medical School merges with the University of Buffalo Medical School.

The first laboratory in the world to be devoted solely to the study of cancer, today known as the Roswell Park Cancer Institute, is founded at the University.

The bearded Dr. Matthew Mann performs surgery at the turn of the century. Courtesy University Archives.

1917 Women picket the White House for the right to vote.

The United States enters World War I and Buffalonians man the U.S. Army Base Hospital Twenty-three in Vittel, France.

1920 The University's Endowment Fund Campaign raises $5 million in ten days from 24,000 subscribers.

1922 Dr. Samuel P. Capen becomes the first full-time chancellor of the University.

1927 Dr. Edward W. Koch, professor of pharmacology and head of the Department of Therapeutics, is named acting dean, then dean. He serves until his death in 1946.

The School of Business Administration (now Management) becomes the University's seventh division.

1940 Buffalo General Hospital is chosen as one of sixty-five hospitals throughout the country to form an army hospital.

1941 Pearl Harbor is bombed and the United States enters World War II.

1943 The antibiotic streptomycin is developed.

1900–1919

1901 President William McKinley is assassinated at the Pan American Exposition.

1904 Mercy Hospital is founded by the Sisters of Mercy.

1905 Charles P. Norton, a lawyer who was active in the founding of the law school and served on its faculty for twenty-one years, becomes acting chancellor of the University. He was instrumental in developing the liberal arts college and transforming the institution into a true university. He bequeathed to the University his entire estate, providing funds for a student union building and for endowment of the University's highest award, the Chancellor's Medal, presented annually since 1925 to an "outstanding citizen of Buffalo."

Of the 689 physicians in Buffalo, 400 graduated from the University.

1909 Site of what is now the South Campus was purchased.

1910 Flexner Report is published.

1912 Dr. Herbert U. Williams, professor of pathology and bacteriology, is named dean.

1913 The University's undergraduate College of Arts and Sciences is founded.

1915 Dr. Thomas H. McKee, associate professor in surgery, is named dean and serves for three years.

1918 Dr. Charles Sumner Jones, associate professor of pediatrics, is named dean and serves until his death in 1927.

The Buffalo City Hospital, today known as the Erie County Medical Center, opens on Grider Street.

1918 World War I ends.

1919 The *Buffalo Medical Journal* is officially merged with the *Medical Review of Reviews* published in New York City due to the difficulty of publishing while a large number of staff were in the military.

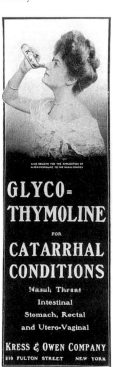

Ad from the 1907 yearbook. Courtesy University Archives.

1920–1939

The Peace Bridge between Buffalo and Fort Erie, Ontario, opens as a memorial to one hundred years of U.S.-Canadian peace.

Hayes Hall, formerly used as the county insane asylum, before being remodeled by the University in the 1920s. Courtesy University Archives.

1929 The stock market crashes, beginning the Great Depression.

1931 The University starts the School of Education.

1936 The School of Nursing begins as a division of the Medical School. The University starts the School of Social Work.

1939 The Graduate School of Arts and Sciences (now simply the Graduate School) becomes an independent division at the University.

David K. Miller, professor of medicine, becomes the first full-time professor in a clinical department.

1940–1959

1945 World War II ends.

1946 Dr. Stockton Kimball, assistant professor of medicine and associate professor of pharmacology, is named acting dean, then dean. He served until his death in 1958.

School of Engineering is established.

Medical School observes its centennial.

Library of the Medical School on High Street. Courtesy University Archives.

1950 Dr. T. Raymond McConnell succeeds Dr. Capen as chancellor and serves until 1954.

The Veterans Administration Hospital is dedicated.

1953 The Medical School moves from High Street to what is now the South Campus at Main and Bailey.

1954 Dr. Clifford C. Furnas, nationally known educator and scientist, becomes the University's ninth chancellor.

1958 Dr. Ernest Witebsky, Distinguished Professor of Bacteriology and Immunology and head of the Department of Bacteriology and Immunology, is named acting dean, then dean. He serves until 1960.

1982   Steven B. Sample becomes president of the University, serving until 1991.

1984   Dean Naughton is named interim vice president for health sciences, then vice president for clinical affairs.

1987   The School changes its name to the School of Medicine and Biomedical Sciences.

1991   William R. Greiner, professor of law and provost, is appointed president of the University.

1960   Dr. Robert L. Brown, assistant professor of medicine, serves as acting dean until 1962.

1962   The private University of Buffalo joins the State University of New York system.

1960–1979

Dr. Douglas M. Surgenor, chairman of the Department of Biochemistry, serves as dean until 1968.

Dr. John D. Stewart becomes vice chancellor for health affairs.

1963   Clifford C. Furnas, now called president of the University, is named acting vice president for health affairs.

1964   Dr. Peter F. Regan is named vice president for health affairs.

1966   School of Health Related Professions is added.

Martin Meyerson, acting chancellor at the University of California at Berkeley, becomes the University's president and serves until 1970.

1967   Dr. Douglas M. Surgenor is named provost of the Faculty of Health Sciences.

1968   Dr. LeRoy A. Pesch, professor of medicine, serves as dean until 1971.

The University at Buffalo awards more than 3,000 degrees in one year—more than were awarded in the first 50 years of its existence.

1969   Dr. Peter F. Regan serves as acting president of the University from September 1969 to July 1970.

1970   Robert L. Ketter, an engineer, becomes president and serves until 1982, supervising the building of the Amherst Campus. Later he was instrumental in bringing the national earthquake center to the University.

Dr. Clyde L. Randall is named vice president for health sciences.

1972   Dr. Clyde L. Randall, vice president for health sciences and professor of gynecology-obstetrics, is named acting dean.

1973   Dr. F. Carter Pannill, professor of medicine, is named vice president for health sciences.

1974   Dr. F. Carter Pannill is named acting dean.

1975   Dr. John Naughton, professor of medicine, is named dean.

1980–1996

1996   Medical School observes its sesquicentennial.

Adler S. The operation on President McKinley. *Scientific American.* 1963;208(3):118-130.

Anderson GL. The story of an educational merger: the State University of New York and the University of Buffalo. *Niagara Frontier.* 1971;18(4):72-84.

Bucki DB. The other enemy: flu. *Buffalo Physician.* 1989-90;23(5):8-13.

Buffalo Medical Journal 1845-1919.

Buffalo Medical Review 1967-1969.

Buffalo Physician 1969-

Bulletin, Medical Society, County of Erie, 1924?-

Cushing H. *The pioneer medical schools of central New York.* New Haven, CT: s.n.; 1934.

Davis AB. With love and money: visiting nursing in Buffalo, New York, 1885-1915. *New York History.* 1990;Jan:45-67.

Drachman VG. The Loomis trial: social mores and obstetrics in the mid-nineteenth century. In: *Health care in America. Essays in social history.* Ed. by Susan Reverby and David Rosner. Philadelphia: Temple University Press; 1979:67-83.

Evans AS. Austin Flint and his contributions to medicine. *Bulletin of the History of Medicine.* 1958;32:224-241.

Flexner A. *Medical education in the United States and Canada; a report to the Carnegie Foundation for the Advancement of Teaching.* New York; 1910.

Flint A. *A memoir of Professor James Platt White, M.D.* Buffalo: Commercial Advertiser Press; 1882.

Hague EB. Development of medical education in Western New York, particularly in Buffalo. *New York State Journal of Medicine.* 1955;55:3311-7.

Hawes E. *Proud Vision. The history of the Buffalo General Hospital. The first hundred years.* New York, NY: Crowell; 1964.

Hill HW. *Municipality of Buffalo, New York. A history 1720-1923.* New York, NY: Lewis; 1923.

Horton JT. *History of Northwestern New York.* New York, NY: Lewis; 1947.

Iris. (Student Yearbook). Buffalo, NY: The students of the University of Buffalo, 1898-1932, 1976-

Javert CT. James Platt White, a pioneer in American obstetrics and gynecology. *Journal of the History of Medicine.* 1948;3(4):489-506.

Jones OP. Confessions of three grave robbers. *Buffalo Physician.* 1981;15(2):12-19.

Jones OP. Health care in Buffalo in 1846. *Buffalo Physician.* 1971;5(4):42-47.

Jones OP. Medical apprenticeships in the early 19th century. *Buffalo Physician.* 1980;14(2):32-40.

Jones OP. A medical student's impression. *Buffalo Physician.* 1977;11(4):44-53.

Jones OP. Our first anatomy professor, James Webster 1803-1854. *Buffalo Physician.* 1973;7(2):8-9.

Jones OP. Our first professor of chemistry and pharmacy, George Hadley 1813-1877. *Buffalo Physician.* 1975;8(4):42-45.

Jones OP. Our first professor of medicine, Austin Flint 1812-1886. *Buffalo Physician.* 1973;7(3):54-61.

Jones OP. Our first professor of obstetrics, James Platt White 1811-1881. *Buffalo Physician.* 1974;8(1):42-47.

Jones OP. Our first professor of pathology and materia medica, Charles Alfred Lee 1801-1872. *Buffalo Physician.* 1974;8(2):18-21.

Jones OP. Our first professor of physiology and medical jurisprudence, Charles B. Coventry 1801-1875. *Buffalo Physician.* 1974;8(3):54-62.

Jones OP. Our first professor of surgery, Frank Hastings Hamilton 1813-1886. *Buffalo Physician.* 1973;7(4):32-35.

Jones OP. Our first teacher. *Buffalo Physician.* 1973;7(1):38-41.

Jones OP. A profile of our first faculty. *Buffalo Physician.* 1975;9(1):16-17.

Jones OP. A student's impression of Austin Flint. *Buffalo Physician.* 1980;14(4):16-20.

Long EH. *University at Buffalo. History, 1846-1904: Departments of Medicine, Pharmacy, Law, Dentistry, Pedagogy.* s.l.: s.n.; 1905?

Matthieu SA. *The medical profession of Erie County, New York. Historical review.* Buffalo, NY: The Medical Society of the County of Erie; 1914.

McKinley Assassination. *Buffalo Medical Journal.* 1901;57(2):205-232 and 271-293.

Medentian. (Student Yearbook). Buffalo, NY: Medical and dental students of the University of Buffalo, 1935-75.

Medentian Magazine. Buffalo, NY: Medical and dental students of the University of Buffalo, 1933-54.

Mirand EA. History of Roswell Park Memorial Institute. *Niagara Frontier.* 1961;8(3):61-69.

Park J. The beginnings of the University of Buffalo. *Niagara Frontier.* 1962;9:7-26.

Park J. *A history of the University of Buffalo.* Buffalo, NY: s.n.; 1917.

Park J. Medicine starts the University. *Niagara Frontier.* 1961;8:48-58.

Park R. Scrapbooks. Located at the University Archives.

Potter WW. 1845-then and now-1895. *Buffalo Medical Journal.* 1895;35(1):65-113.

Rahn H. Brief history of the Department of Physiology at State University of New York at Buffalo 1846-1986. *Physiologist.* 1986;29(5, Suppl.):1-6.

Sartwell PE. The case of the poisoned well. A reconstruction based on three papers by Austin Flint. *American Journal of Epidemiology.* 1971;93(3):150-156.

Sentz L. Buffalo Medical Journal. *Bulletin of the Medical Library Association.* 1985;73(3):278-282. Reprinted in *Buffalo Physician.* 1987;21(3):10-13.

Smith HP. *History of the City of Buffalo and Erie County.* Syracuse, NY: Mason; 1884.

Talbott JH. Bench marks. *Buffalo Medical Review.* 1967;1(1):3-28.

This university—these restless men. Amherst, NY: Office of University Publications; 1986.

Walsh JJ. *History of medicine in New York. Three centuries of medical progress.* New York, NY: National Americana Society; 1919.

Wiggin BL. Albert J. Myer, pioneer meteorologist. *Niagara Frontier.* 1970;17(4):92-99.

Wolfson I. The influence of the Erie Canal on medical education and practice in Upstate New York. *New York State Journal of Medicine.* 1955;55:2524-2527.

Woodward JS. *Men of Medicine in Erie County 1821-1971.* Buffalo: Medical Society, County of Erie; 1971.

Index

Index

dormitories, 115, 128
Dorsette, Cornelius, 118

E

Eastman, Sandford, 34, 183
Eccles, John C., 155
Elizabeth Blackwell Society, 126
Emergency Hospital, Pan American
    Exposition, 41, 60, 61
Emergency Hospital, Sisters, 92
Erie Canal, 12
Erie County Hospital, 79, 98, 99, 100
Erie County Medical Center, 100, 106

F

Fairfield Medical School, 15, 19, 20
Farber Hall, 50, 153
Fillmore, Millard, President, 15, 17, 23,
    182
Flexner Report, 65, 66, 68, 133
Flint, Austin, 13, 15, 18, 19, 24, 28,
    29, 32, 33, 36, 38, 116, 182
Flint Murmur, 32
follies, Medical School, 130
Foster Hall, 135
Fox, Katherine, 38
Fox, Margaret, 38
fraternities, 114, 115, 126
Fronczak Hall, 79
Fronczak, Francis E., 79
fund raising, 15, 23, 54, 132, 133, 134,
    136, 164
Furnas, Clifford C., 184, 185

G

Gage, Andrew, 157
Geneva Medical College, 15, 19, 20,
    21, 116
Gibson, James A., 74
Gibson, James A., Anatomical Society,
    74, 126
Goodale, Walter S., 82, 100, 101, 123,
    143
Gottlieb, Bernhardt, 124
Gram, Franklin C., 82
Gratwick, William, Mrs., 96
grave robbing, 39
Greatbatch, Wilson, 157
Green, E. B., 144
Greene, Clayton, 142, 143, 151
Greene, David, 142

Greiner, William R., 177, 185
Griffith, Fred R., 148
Guthrie, Robert, 157

H

Hadley, George, 18, 20, 34, 183
Hamilton, Frank Hastings, 15, 18, 20,
    28, 33, 182
Harrington Lectureship, 35
Harrington, Devillo W., 35
Hartman, Frank A., 133, 140, 176
Hauptman, Herbert, 173
Hayes Hall, 27, 125, 144
Hayes, Edmund, General, 67, 125
Health Sciences Library, 134, 144, 164,
    170, 171, 172
Hill, John Davidson, 38
Hochstetter, Ralph, 152
homeopathy, 42, 86
hospitals, 27, 28, 29, 30, 34, 35, 41,
    46, 47, 48, 60, 61, 71, 75, 76, 77,
    79, 86–109, 138, 139, 149, 150
Howe, Lucian, 91
Hubbell, Alvin, 56
Hurrell, M. Louise, 77

I

I.C.I. Society, 115
Ilahi-Baksh, Grace 119
influenza, 67, 76, 82, 84, 85
Iris, 115
International Medicine, Society on, 129
Italian-American Club, 121

J

Jewett, Theodore C., Jr., 172
Johnson, Ebenezer, 182
Jones, Charles Sumner, 184
Jones, Oliver P., 154
Jones, W. Yerby, 122

K

Karle, Jerome, 173
Ketter, Robert L., 185
Kimball, Stockton, 145, 151, 184
Klendshoj, Niels, 141
Knox, Grace, 67
Knox, Seymour H., 160
Koch, Edward W., 184

Index

Index